SIR FREDERICK TREVES

*The Extra-Ordinary
Edwardian*

SIR FREDERICK TREVES

The Extra-Ordinary
Edwardian

STEPHEN TROMBLEY

ROUTLEDGE

In memory of
Robert Trombley
and for
Meryl, Brian, Adrienne and David

First published 1989
by Routledge
11 New Fetter Lane, London EC4P 4EE
29 West 35th Street, New York, NY 10001

© 1989 S. Trombley

Photoset and printed in Great Britain by
Redwood Burn Limited, Trowbridge, Wiltshire

British Library Cataloguing in Publication Data
Trombley, Stephen
Treves.
1. Medicine. Treves, Sir Frederick,
1853–1923
I. Title
610′.92′4

Library of Congress Cataloging in Publication Data
Trombley, Stephen.
Treves: The Extra-Ordinary Edwardian / Stephen Trombley.
p. cm.
Bibliography: p.
Includes index.
1. Treves, Frederick, Sir, 1853–1923. 2. Surgeons –
England –
Biography. I. Title.
RD27.35.T74T76 1989
617′.092′4—DC19 88–39493
[B]

ISBN 0-415-03423-X

CONTENTS

ACKNOWLEDGEMENTS

This book would never have been written without the generous co-operation of people who gave freely of their time and knowledge. My thanks must go first of all to the Treves family: Frederick and Jean Treves and Vivien and Philip Judd. I am also grateful to Georgina Battiscombe, Dr Peter Beale, Ivor Beavis, K. Carter, Professor Brian E. D. Cooke, E. H. Cornelius, Philip Neale Dawe, Jennifer Duffin, John Entract, Desmond Flower, Thea Hunter, Frank K. Lorenz, Dr W. S. Macdonald, David Macmillan, Virginia Murray, M. R. Perkin, Charles P. C. Pettit, M. N. Slade and Colonel A. V. Tennuci.

The staffs of the following libraries gave help and advice over a long period: The Wellcome Library; Senate House Library, University of London; and the library of the Royal College of Surgeons.

Letters and other documents from the Royal Archive at Windsor are quoted by gracious permission of Her Majesty the Queen. I am also indebted to the (then) librarian of the Royal Archive, Sir Robin Mackworth-Young and to the registrar, Miss Jane Langton and her staff for their kind assistance.

My agent Andrew Best of Curtis Brown has been, as usual, critical and helpful throughout. My editor Andrew Wheatcroft had the courage to take on an unwieldy manuscript and make crucial suggestions for revision. Denise O'Hagan nursed the book through press. Catherine Trombley suggested I write it and compiled the index. But my greatest debt is to the late Murray Mindlin, whose passion for knowledge and love is sorely missed.

INTRODUCTION

Frederick Treves is best known to a contemporary audience as the surgeon who befriended Joseph Merrick – the unfortunate Elephant Man. Yet, without that distinction, he would justify a biographer's labours. Relentlessly ambitious, he became surgeon to four successive monarchs, beginning with the Duke of York (later King George V). The high point of his royal career was the successful appendix operation he performed on King Edward VII on the eve of his coronation. In his day he was the foremost teacher and practitioner of anatomy and surgery in England. As a civilian surgeon he returned from the Boer War angry at the antiquated methods of the Royal Army Medical Corps, and was largely responsible for the reforms which put it on a modern footing. He was a founding member of the British Red Cross Society, and the first president of its national executive. In his later years he was the best-selling author of a shelf of travel books.

Treves's was a life of ambition and duty, a public life. He was a charismatic teacher and operator who influenced a generation of surgeons. He was an unusually observant witness to significant events of his time. And he was more than a mere servant of the court: he was an intimate of Queen Alexandra; and King Edward VII came to rely not only upon his surgical skills and his friendship, but on his judgement in matters of medical and social policy.

But Treves was also an individualist, a man capable of both radical and conservative views. And he was a controversialist. There was nothing he liked better than to be at the centre of a political row or a professional intrigue.

Why, then, did he not write his autobiography? The answer lies in a meeting between him and his publisher and close friend Newman Flower in 1921. By then Treves had retired to Vevey to devote himself to writing. Flower put it to Treves that his life had been quite remarkable; remarkable enough in itself, but even more so given the long list of famous patients he had treated. Surely this was the material of autobiography? Treves agreed it probably was, though he added, 'people don't want to read my muck' – a piece of false modesty if there ever was one.

Treves had always been a fast worker. A few months later Flower received a manuscript which he judged to be the most promising material for an autobiography that he had ever had the good fortune to read.

A week later, Treves was in London. Flower received an urgent telephone call, asking for a meeting at Treves's bank – immediately. Would Flower bring the manuscript with him? Flower arrived to find his friend pacing nervously up and down in front of the safe deposit boxes. Without a word, Treves seized the manuscript and locked it away. When the dumbfounded publisher asked what was the matter, Treves explained that he had been speaking to a medical colleague who warned that he must not, on any account, publish details of his patients in an autobiography. He had got the wind up, and was frightened to publish. It was a publisher's nightmare, and Flower's disappointment turned to exasperation when he learned that the doctor who warned Treves against publication happened to be the medical director of his own firm, Cassells. Treves took Flower to the Marlborough Club for a consolation lunch and promised to write a book about his unknown patients. The result was *The Elephant Man and Other Reminiscences* (1923), his last book and arguably his best.

So much for autobiography. But why has no biographer turned his hand to such a rich subject? The answer again involves Newman Flower. After her husband's death, Lady Treves asked Flower to visit her in the spring of 1924. She knew how much Treves valued Flower's friendship, and that he was not only an accomplished writer, but could publish any book he chose at Cassells. He was an obvious choice of biographer and publisher. He persuaded Lady Treves to hand over the manuscript which still lay in the bank, along with other vital documents.

After he had completed nearly a year's work on the project, Flower was once again summoned by Lady Treves. The silence which hung over the tea cups did not bode well for him. Lady Treves began by asking him to omit from the biography any mention of her husband's work at court. The astonished Flower protested that this would cut the heart out of the book. Lady Treves explained that when Treves's senior medical colleague at court, Sir Francis Laking, had died, the court asked Lady Laking to return the King's letters. She expressed her fear that should Flower intend to use the King's letters in his biography, the court might ask her to do the same. She did not want to take that risk. Flower argued that without the King's letters, the book would be a farce, killed at birth by the critics. In that case, Lady Treves replied, her husband's memory should survive in history by the work he did. And that was that.

In fact, Treves had bequeathed to his wife all his papers, with an instruction to destroy his case books and any other papers she saw fit. In the end she destroyed most of them, including the manuscript autobiography.

It would seem then that a biography of Treves is fated from the start. Nevertheless, the effort seems worth making, despite the absence of the kind of intimate material which has become the cornerstone of modern biography.

This is not a book which can lay claim to any kind of methodological sophistication. It is in some ways a public life, relying as it does on Treves's published work and on numerous accounts and reminiscences of him. Yet I hope I have achieved something of the personal, in spite of the handicap under which I have laboured. Treves's writing – even in his scientific papers – is often intensely personal, offering many glimpses into his private views on a very wide range of subjects.

So far as I am able to know my subject by seven years' acquaintance, I believe this is a portrait he might recognize, and that my errors and omissions would elicit his laughter rather than his anger.

Chapter One

YOUTH

In the spring of 1877 four people are gathered in a tiny sitting room in Derbyshire. One is a twenty-five year old woman who is lying on a sofa. Her complexion is pallid, her breathing tortured. The corners of her mouth are sore and excoriated. Her tongue looks more like a dog's: unnaturally red, smooth, thin. She has great difficulty swallowing. Her fingernails, once shapely, have become brittle and concave.

Her husband is sitting anxiously. He is older, about thirty. Dressed in his Sunday best. Scrubbed clean – the others can smell the harsh home-made soap on him.

Sitting next to him is a local physician, William Webb. He is forty-four. He is unable to hide his apprehension.

The youngest person in the room is leaning over the woman, taking her pulse and talking to her in quiet, soothing tones. He is twenty-four years old, just qualified from the London Hospital. He has only lived in Wirksworth a fortnight, having taken a junior partnership in the local practice of William Milligan.

The contrast between doctor and patient is startling. The doctor is of medium height but with broad shoulders and chest and well-developed arms. He could be an athlete, though he is a little on the stocky side. His hair is dark, very fine, parted on the left and combed casually across his forehead in a nearly successful attempt to hide the fact that it is receding. He wears a walrus moustache which makes him look a little older than he is. He wears the costume of his trade: a black frock coat and waistcoat, across which hangs a heavy gold watch chain. A silk handkerchief dangles carelessly from the inside breast pocket of his coat. He is wearing spectacles as he measures the pulse, but removes them when he has finished.

Gently disengaging himself from the woman, the young doctor

confers with his older colleague. There is no doubt about the diagnosis: pernicious anaemia. But there has been some doubt about the treatment. Milligan and the other senior partners in the young man's practice agree that the woman has only weeks to live. Bed rest and tonic is their prescription. The young doctor disagrees. There may be a slight chance for her if a blood transfusion is attempted. Milligan and his partners point out that he has never done a blood transfusion. The young man argues that neither have they, and seeks the advice of Webb: the competition. Webb gives the operation little chance of success, but decides to support his young colleague and act as his assistant.

It is twenty-three years before Karl Landsteiner will discover blood groups and their importance for choosing compatible blood donors. It is thirty-eight years before Richard Lewisohn will perfect the technique of transfusion.

At two o'clock Webb asks the woman's husband to strip to the waist and leads him to a sofa at the opposite end of the room from his wife. Webb holds his arm while the young doctor draws ten ounces of blood. Before the syringe is full, the man faints. Webb bandages his arm and wraps him in his own coat. The young doctor empties the syringe of blood into a vessel which he floats in water kept at 105° Fahrenheit. He tries to keep the blood defibrinated by whipping it with two silver forks and by straining it through muslin.

While Webb continues stirring the blood, the young doctor makes an incision in the median cephalic vein in the woman's arm. He later reports that she was so weak she did not notice him making the incision. He quickly passes a silk suture under the vein in readiness for the operation.

He takes the home-made transfusion apparatus he has fashioned the night before: a three-ounce brass ear syringe with a long ivory nozzle sharpened to a point. Lifting the suture, he is able to hold the vein tight against the syringe. Three times he injects her husband's blood into her vein.

The operation has an immediate effect. The woman becomes animated. Her breathing and pulse increase dramatically. She speaks. She takes some wine and water. Soon she complains of being too warm and attempts to remove the bedclothes. The doctors prepare hot water bottles which they place at her feet, thighs, loins. They cover her chest in flannels wrung out in boiling water. They think the operation may have been a success.

But at three o'clock their hopes fade. The woman's temperature begins to drop and her pulse gradually fades. At six o'clock she dies.

A few months later the young doctor publishes a paper in the *Lancet*: 'Anaemia treated by transfusion: A case of failure'. He writes:

> In the advance of all medical science, and more especially in the attainment of true principles as to treatment, a record of failures is perhaps as important as records of success. No scientific principle is more trustworthy than that which has been arrived at by a process of elimination of error, and no plan of practice more reliable than that which has been the outcome of constant searchings and many failures.
>
> (Treves 1877)

It is often said of surgeons that they bury their failures. It is remarkable that a surgeon so young should choose to publicize, in his first medical paper, a failure.

The details of this episode are preserved not in a personal case book or in a letter, but in a scientific paper for a medical journal. Already we have a clue to Treves's character. A first-rate scientist, he yet eschews the jargon of academia and the convention of impersonality in writing. He treats the woman as a human being, tells *their* story – the story of doctor and patient – and concludes with an observation on the nature of medical empiricism.

The paper tells us a great deal, too, about the age in which Treves began his medical career. While antiseptic and aseptic methods had been discovered by Lister in 1865, they are not in common use in 1877. Even if Treves had by good fortune found a donor of a compatible blood type, he probably would have killed his patient through infection.

* * *

Treves came from Dorset, whose landscape was to have an overwhelming influence on him. It gave him an eye for natural beauty; but it was more the landscape of Thomas Hardy's tragic novels than the perspective of the Sunday watercolourist that stayed with him. Reminiscing about Dorset at the age of seventy, Treves's imagination was fired by the plight of the agricultural labourer who, far from living in a rural idyll, endured circumstances which he judged to be worse than those of the slaves in British colonies. His interest in the topography of

Dorset had a profound effect on his later work as an anatomist, for his system of anatomy is no more than a topography of the human interior.

Dorset's proximity to the sea gave him an early passion for the romance of pirates, buccaneers, explorers and builders of empire, and a celebration of the sea and the men who navigate it was to form a central theme of his travel books. In his youth and middle age he devoted a great deal of time to learning the mariner's craft – he earned his Master Mariner's certificate – and sailing was one of the few relaxations he allowed himself in a busy career. During the heyday of his career at the London Hospital, he would regularly cross the English Channel single-handed on Boxing Day.

This sailing for pleasure was evidence of the extent to which Treves had asserted his ability and ambition against the fairly routine existence of his forebears. The Treves family belonged to that class formerly described as the yeomanry: solid, land-owning folk. There is nothing in Treves's pedigree to suggest the distinction he would achieve. His great grandfather, Joseph Treves, was an innkeeper in the village of Stratton, about five miles northwest of Dorchester. Little is known of him, but his great grandson's aversion to drink (and Treves would later write pamphlets for the Church of England Temperance Society) suggests that the family was happy to have risen above that station.

Treves's grandfather, William (1744–1829), was apprenticed as a cabinet maker and upholsterer. Having mastered his trade, he moved to Dorchester and set up a shop in Cornhill – a most respectable address in the heart of the county town. William enjoyed immediate success, and at the age of twenty-two was secure enough to marry Elizabeth Greening, by whom he had three children: Philip, William (Frederick's father), and Elizabeth. Soon William was able to take on an apprentice, and his business continued to flourish until his death.

We find an early clue to Frederick's character in his grandfather's will. The only education William had was that offered by the local school, but he clearly had aspirations beyond that. His estate included many books and pictures, an indication of the extent to which he desired to improve his lot and that of his children.

A further clue to William's ambition to raise the status of his family is the careful way he arranged for his estate to be managed after his death. He left his stock in trade to his elder son Philip and his friend John Pett who, it may be presumed, was prevailed upon to offer the guidance of an experienced older man as a form of insuring the business against failure.

But Philip was an ironmonger rather than an upholsterer, and things did not work out under his management. Four years after his father's death, Philip's younger brother William took over the business in Cornhill. William was only seventeen when his father died, and at twenty-one he assumed a grave responsibility. The family's hopes were pinned on him. From his father's former premises at number 102 Cornhill he carefully nurtured the business until, by 1851, he was employing thirteen men. Ten years later he was employing sixteen men and two apprentices, and had moved to larger and more prestigious premises at number 108 Cornhill.

In 1842 Frederick's father married Jane Knight, a Devon girl. He was thirty, she was twenty-eight – their ages indicating the conservative attitude both sides of the family brought to the management of their affairs. Jane was a strong woman who took the business of marriage and motherhood seriously. She perceived her role as that of teacher and enforcer of good morals and good hygiene. The Bible was her text, providing her with the authority to lead the family and with comfort in her later years.

William and Jane had six children. The first, William Knight Treves, was born in 1843 and became a lasting source of pride to his parents because he would rise from tradesman to professional by becoming a doctor – the first of three William and Jane would produce. William's career was relatively distinguished. After the usual period in general practice – in which he might have been expected to languish – he became a leading expert on scrofula (glandular swelling, later recognized as tuberculosis) and built a lucrative practice in Margate.

In the five years after William's birth, Jane was constantly with child, producing Jane (1845), Frances (1847) and Edward (1848), the last of whom would also pursue a medical career. After an interval of five years, two more children were born: Frederick (1853) and Mary Elizabeth (1854). With six children to feed, the industrious and cautious William decided to expand his business beyond cabinet making and upholstering to include appraising, carpet warehousing and undertaking.

William was an affectionate but demanding father. When his son William Knight left home to attend St Thomas's Hospital medical school, he wrote more letters than is perhaps usual from father to son.

5

Though they are warm, they contain an element of anxious hectoring. The father is concerned to ensure that his son does well in examinations, that he is mixing with the right crowd and that he is attending church regularly (he suggests a suitable preacher in Camberwell). Family news is left for Jane to communicate, but her letters also reiterate the family's anxiety about academic success, social hygiene and religious attendance.

For Frederick, the chief influence of his youth was William Barnes, the Dorset poet who ran a small school in South Street. Barnes is known today as a minor poet who wrote in the Dorset dialect. But his achievement as a thinker and teacher was far greater, and in his school Treves had his first exposure to the kind of wide-ranging intelligence he admired most. Barnes was an accomplished artist, engraver and musician. He knew many languages, both living and dead. He was a keen amateur naturalist and archaeologist whose personal collection of fossils and other artefacts forms the basis of the present Dorchester Museum collections. Perhaps the most important influence that Barnes had on Treves was his belief that all areas of knowledge are connected, and he may be seen as an early practitioner of a multidisciplinary approach to education. He also believed that education should avoid rote learning and instil the ability to think and to solve problems.

Even in 1860, Barnes seemed to the young Treves a kind of historical apparition. He had white hair and a long beard, and always wore knee breeches and shoes with large buckles. Striding about Dorchester in his cap and cape, with a large bag over his shoulder and a stout staff in his hand, he seemed a figure from another age. For young Frederick, he made it seem as though history was alive.

Every morning Frederick would be taken to the school in South Street by the maid, Jane Honeybun, who would also collect him at the end of the day. Both William Barnes and Thomas Hardy's sister Mary recalled that Treves was so shy that if Jane was not there to collect him precisely when school had finished, he would hide in the cloakroom. His shyness was not to last long.

Barnes's poetry and teaching was the link which bound Treves and Thomas Hardy, and Hardy always felt a sentimental attachment to Treves because it was from his father's shop that he bought his first writing desk – an object which he cherished, and which was without a scratch upon his death.

In 1867 the long established order of the Treveses in Dorset was smashed. On 20 July, after a short illness, William Treves died. He was fifty-five, the precise age at which his father before him had died. Jane Treves acted quickly. Within two months the business was sold and the family established at Rest Villa in Loughborough Road, Kennington – a modest, middle class address in south London. On the day he left Dorchester, Frederick carved his initials on a tree in the wood near Came golf links. His handiwork would still be there when he returned as an elderly and distinguished tourist.

In the autumn of 1867 Frederick enrolled at the Merchant Taylors' school. He was only an average student, preferring the playing field to the classroom. Nine months later, tragedy struck. Frederick's sister Mary Elizabeth died of intussusception of the large intestine. She was thirteen. In a few short years, Frederick would be an expert in the treatment of her condition.

Thus began his long apprenticeship with death.

Chapter Two

SURGERY

In 1871, when Treves left Merchant Taylors', medicine as a profession was only beginning to enjoy the respect it does today. As a body of scientific knowledge, it had only recently emerged from the half metaphysical, half practical humoral pathology of Galen. The social standing of the profession had been low, and the pedigree of the barber surgeon ensured that doctors would continue to be caricatured in the popular cultures of the day as vain and blustering incompetents. Within the profession, the standing of the physician was much higher than that of the surgeon, the gruesome practicalities of surgery seeming less elegant than the bedside pronouncements of smartly dressed men who wrote prescriptions and advised bed rest.

At that time the licensing of doctors was controlled by three bodies: the Royal College of Physicians, the Royal College of Surgeons and the Society of Apothecaries. The distinction was class-ridden and hierarchical. In Treves's time, for instance, only graduates of Oxford or Cambridge could become fellows of the Royal College of Physicians. Members could not belong to either of the other bodies, or practise surgery or follow the apothecary's trade. The physician's powerful standing in the profession derived from this exclusivity. Even William Harvey, who had studied at Padua, was required to obtain a Cambridge degree by 'incorporation' before he was admitted to the college. While he answered the committee's questions satisfactorily, they decided to give him tacit permission to practice, but withheld membership until he re-presented himself for further examination. Such was the power of the college.

The physicians could feel superior to the surgeons because their college was founded in 1518, while the Royal College of Surgeons of England was finally established only in 1843 (The Royal College of

8

Surgeons of London having been founded in 1800). Unlike the physicians who were university educated, the surgeons – until Treves's day – were apprenticed. Their activity was therefore considered more a craft than the professional practice of a science. And, it must be said, until surgery was grounded in true principles of anatomy, the judgement was a fairly accurate one.

At the bottom of the professional tree was the Society of Apothecaries. Originally part of the Grocer's Company of the City of London, the society's royal charter dated from 1617 and in 1815 the Apothecaries Act allowed the society to grant a licence (LSA) for medical practice following a period of apprenticeship.

Treves's class origins would deny him access to medicine through the Royal College of Physicians. But surgery, in retrospect, was a wise choice, even if it was largely dictated by economic and social circumstances, as three factors were conspiring to raise it from the level of a barbarous craft to a precise, effective and humane science. First, the control of pain from the middle of the nineteenth century by the introduction of anaesthetics meant not only that the patient endured less pain, but that the surgeon had a longer time in which to operate. The swashbuckling heroics of surgeons who could amputate a leg in seconds were replaced by careful operating technique. Second, Lister's discovery of antisepsis reduced the risk of infection, which improved the patient's chances of survival after surgery by a large margin. And third, the growth of the science of anatomy resulted in the establishing of an accurate map of the organs and an understanding of their function, and thus both diagnosis and operative technique were placed on a firm scientific basis.

These developments meant that surgery was entering its golden age. During Treves's lifetime it would advance far more rapidly and dramatically than medicine. Treves's career starts, then, on the verge of a revolution in which success could be rewarded not only by professional satisfaction, but by fame and fortune as well.

*   *   *

In 1871 Treves spent some months at University College London, which had been established in 1827 to provide an education to those who were excluded from Oxford or Cambridge by virtue of class or religion (the great universities being unreformed then). University College specialized in science and medicine, and quickly established a modern and forward-thinking curriculum which was considered by many to be superior to the old methods of Oxford and Cambridge.

Treves was fortunate in that by the time he was ready to begin his surgical studies, the great teaching hospitals had established medical schools which offered a more organized and systematic education than that provided by the old method of apprenticeship. Treves chose the London Hospital in Whitechapel Road in the East End of London. It is in some respects a curious choice, as his brother William had qualified at St Thomas's – rather higher up the social scale of hospitals at the time.

There are numerous reasons why Treves might have chosen the London. At that time it had the largest surgical ward of any hospital in the country and boasted some very good teachers on its staff. It was located in one of the poorest areas of London, and for some reason had a history of attracting socially-minded students, particularly from Scotland, who involved themselves in the problems of the community. And the problems were legion. Being one of the most densely populated areas of the city, the East End suffered more than its share of infectious diseases through poor housing and bad sanitation. Because of its proximity to the London docks, it was a gateway for diseases originating all over the world. There were four separate cholera epidemics in the early nineteenth century, to which one could add the diseases already endemic in the area: tuberculosis, typhoid, typhus and deficiency disease.

The hospital also provided its students with more acute surgical cases than any other in the country. Many of these were a direct result of the working conditions of the poor. Long hours, bad diet and unsafe conditions combined to cause alarming numbers of industrial accidents. It was a common occurrence, when Treves first arrived at the London, to see the badly mangled body of a docker being carried in by his friends on a plank or shutter.

At that time English hospitals were voluntary, supported by the subscriptions of benefactors who then became governors. Becoming a governor allowed one to recommend patients for admission. While the hospitals existed to serve those in need, this service was rendered at a certain cost – moral, if not financial. The benefactors, who were usually professed Christians, expected discharged patients to render thanks first to them, and second to the Lord. At the London, the committee would meet each Thursday at eleven a.m. (latecomers had to put a shilling in the poor box). First those patients presented cured by the physician, then those presented cured by the surgeon, were called in and required to thank their benefactors. They were then instructed to visit their parish church and thank God for the cure they had received through the benefactors' charity. Some patients refused to offer such thanks, assuming that medical treatment was their right. A blacklist of names was kept and those refusing thanks to God and man were barred from further treatment at the hospital. Those who gave thanks were awarded a certificate which would admit them to the hospital in future. After such meetings the committee regularly adjourned to The Angel and Crown to conduct the remaining business.

The administrative structure of the hospital was not the only primitive thing about it. The receiving room where patients arrived was a filthy area presided over by a stern matron whom Treves observed to be generally the worse for drink. The diseased, the injured, and the drunk all competed for attention, while surgeons and dressers in adjoining rooms worked in equally filthy conditions. While asepsis was known, it was not always practised. Dressers licked catgut sutures to thread dirty needles. Furniture and walls were splattered with blood. In the first ward on which Treves worked, there was only one sponge with which to tend the surgical wounds of all the patients.

Nevertheless, in addition to a large number of surgical cases, what the London offered its students was a distinguished teaching staff. During Treves's student days these included Sir Hughlings Jackson, one of the founders of modern neurology, and Sir Jonathan Hutchinson, one of the greatest surgeons of his day. Hutchinson had a profound influence on Treves, and the qualities for which he is noted apply equally to his pupil. He was a prolific writer (a selection from his writings, *The Archives of Surgery*, runs to ten volumes); he was a brilliant diagnostician; and he was an exceptional teacher. Hutchinson was like William Barnes in that he had a tendency to link apparently disparate areas of knowledge, so that a lecture which began on the anatomy of the whale might end with a disquisition on the poetry of Wordsworth.

Treves's description of Jackson's teaching method could well apply to himself:

He made teaching interesting by the ingenuity of his arguments
. . . [he] generalised philosophically and took broad views,

avoiding text book formalism. . . . He would further demonstrate the case by reference to allied cases, to cases dissimilar, and to conditions that were at first showing apparently incongruous. He would then take a general view of the matter in hand, regarding the case before him as an item in a widely extending series.

(Hutchinson 1946)

Apart from the teaching of great men like Jackson and Hutchinson, the London also offered innovation in terms of new techniques and equipment. Herbert Davies was one of the first English physicians to employ the stethoscope; Sir Morell Mackenzie was friends with Czermak, inventor of the laryngoscope, which he introduced to England; and John Couper, who had studied under Lister in Edinburgh, introduced his master's teachings to the London and invented the magazine ophthalmoscope to measure errors of refraction and degrees of astigmatism. All of these developments influenced Treves, who was inspired to invent numerous surgical devices and techniques of his own – not all of them successful.

Unlike most of his contemporaries, Treves was to develop an interest in the history of medicine, which he considered, much in advance of his time, to be relevant to contemporary practice. This interest was stimulated and nurtured by Walter Rivington, who was dismissed by some of his colleagues as a poor operator and 'an uneven teacher at the bedside'. Nevertheless, his massive 1,200 page history, *The Medical Profession*, is a classic which was written in only nine months for the Carmichael Prize of 1879. It covers the history of medicine from antiquity to the end of the nineteenth century, and is a work without equal in its time. Its influence on Treves was enormous.

The academic year at the London was divided into winter and summer sessions for which students paid eighty-four guineas per annum. Teaching of the full range of medical disciplines took place on male and female wards of thirty beds each. Every afternoon at three-thirty practical morbid anatomy was taught in the post-mortem room, supervised by Hughlings–Jackson and the great pathologist Henry Sutton, who influenced Treves's belief that all surgical knowledge had to be based on anatomical knowledge. It was in the post-mortem room that Treves became a surgeon.

Despite the presence of so many good teachers, education at the London could be rather haphazard. An anonymous writer reminisced of Treves's student days:

The teaching on the medical side can scarcely be described, really no representation pertained to it; visits were made in the mornings by some; an occasional notice posted that an 'Auscultation class would take place on a certain date' which as often as not never came off; clinical lectures too were like flowers in winter.

The students were often loutish and given to practical jokes. One teacher of obstetrics, R. F. Ramsbotham, was a particular butt of the students' jokes. His constantly calm demeanour only increased their efforts, which culminated in one student accepting a bet that he would not let a monkey loose in Ramsbotham's class. He did, and the monkey perched on the back of the teacher's chair, causing great mirth as the portly doctor struggled to rise and exit with dignity.

Each week, two students were appointed residents under the house surgeon. They were responsible for all surgical and accident cases for that week. No leave was allowed. They were given a diet of porridge for breakfast, bread, butter, cheese and beer for lunch and a 'regal' evening meal. When not on duty, our anonymous informant tells us, billiards, cards and skittles were the main preoccupations of the medical students – 'The first and third was amply provided for by a house in Bedford Square, and the second by The Good Samaritan, which had an upstairs room specially reserved for the pastime.'

By the mid-1880s, when Treves had returned to the London as a teacher, things had not changed much. In his autobiography, Sir Wilfred Grenfell (who was one of Treves's pupils), wrote: 'Looking back, I am grateful to my alma mater, and have that real affection for her that every loyal son should have. But even that does not conceal from me how poor a teaching establishment it was.' He continues:

> Those who had natural genius, and the advantages of previous scientific training, who were sons of medical men, or had served apprenticeships to them, need not have suffered so much through its utter inefficiency. But men in my position suffered quite unconsciously a terrible handicap, and it was only the influences for which I had nothing to thank the hospital that saved me from the catastrophes which overtook so many who started with me.
>
> (Grenfell 1922)

The coarse behaviour of his fellow students was something for which

Grenfell's refined sensibility was unprepared. He speaks of being 'flung into a coarse and evil environment, among men who too often took pride in their shame'. As for the medical teaching, he writes:

> Examinations . . . were practically race committees; they did no teaching, but when you had done certain things, they allowed you to come up and be examined, and if you got through a written and a 'viva voce' examination you were inflicted on an unsuspecting public 'qualified to kill' – often only too literally so.
>
> (Grenfell 1922)

Grenfell relates how students were required to sign up for the various obligatory lectures. In many cases, 'this was simply a matter of tipping the beadle, who marked you off'. Grenfell confesses that he attended only two botany lectures during the entire course. His experience on both occasions persuaded him not to return.

> At the first some practical joker had spilled a solution of carbon bisulphide all over the professor's platform, and the smell was so intolerable that the lecture was prorogued. At the second, some wag let loose a couple of pigeons, whereupon everyone started either to capture them or stir them up with pea-shooters. The professor said, 'Gentlemen, if you do not wish to learn, you are at liberty to leave.' The entire class walked out. The insignificant sum of two and sixpence secured me my sign-up for the remainder of the course.
>
> (Grenfell 1922)

Other medical subjects fared no better.

> *Materia medica* was almost identical, and while we had better fortune with physiology, no experience and no apparatus for verifying its teachings were even shown us. Our chemistry professor was a very clever man, but extremely eccentric, and his class was pandemonium. I have seen him so frequently pelted with peas, when his head was turned, as to force him to leave the amphitheatre in despair. I well remember also an unpopular student being pushed down from the top row almost on to the experiment table. There was practically no histology taught, and little or no pathology. Almost every bit of the microscope which I did was learned on my own instrument at home. Anatomy, however, we were well-taught in the dissecting room, where we could easily obtain all the work we needed. But not till Sir

Frederick Treves became our lecturer in anatomy and surgery
was it worth doing more than pay the necessary sum to get
signed up.

(Grenfell 1922)

Without being branded a swot, Treves ran the gauntlet of a medical
education at the London, emerging as one of its finest products.

Chapter Three

BRILLIANCE

Treves published his first scientific paper during his second year as a medical student ('The relation between the odour of gases and their power of resisting liquefaction', 1872) and qualified as a licentiate of the Society of Apothecaries in 1874. His teachers were excited when, in the following year, he passed his membership examinations for the Royal College of Surgeons on his first try – an unusual feat in itself, and even more unusual for a man of twenty-two (most students normally passed on their second or third attempt around the age of twenty-six). He rounded off his medical education by serving as house surgeon at the London from May to August of 1876.

Meanwhile, Frederick's brother William had become resident surgeon at the Royal National Hospital for Scrofula in Margate, and had established his own practice in partnership with William Hunter and William Thornton. In 1901 William was appointed consultant surgeon to the hospital, and he remained in Margate for the rest of his life. Though less brilliant than his younger brother, William was a successful and highly respected doctor (he later became District Medical Officer and Medical Officer of Health). Midway through his career he gave up private practice to devote himself entirely to the study and surgical treatment of tuberculosis, or scrofula as some manifestations continued to be known even after Koch's discovery of the tubercle bacillus in 1882. He perfected an operation which left the patient relatively unscarred, and it was largely due to his work that Margate became the centre of tuberculosis treatment in Britain for many years.

In August 1876 Frederick accepted an invitation from William to take on a five-month appointment at the Margate hospital. Fascinated by this new area of study, Frederick resolved to become an expert on scrofula. Within weeks he had started research on what was to be his first book, *Scrofula and Its Gland Diseases* (1882). His elder brother did not publish his own (and only) work, *On The Diagnosis and Treatment of Scrofulous Glands*, until 1899. Despite their professional rivalry, the brothers maintained a close friendship and would regularly sail and fish together off the west country coast.

Frederick's time at Margate was happy and restful. Though he worked hard on research for his book, his duties at the hospital and in his brother's practice were not onerous. Later one of Frederick's students at the London, D. G. Halsted, would describe what a summer working for William Treves was like:

> I used to drive around Margate that summer in a gig drawn by a smashing pair of cobs, attending to nothing more serious than a few rich and elderly hypochondriacs, and having a splendid time swimming and playing tennis. Curiously enough, I never even met Knight Treves, but his brother's recommendation was a good enough introduction as far as he was concerned.
>
> (Halsted 1959)

During this summer idyll Frederick was courting Anne Elizabeth Mason, also from Dorchester. In Annie, Frederick found precisely what he was looking for in a wife. She was a devout Christian who believed in the values of hard work and devotion to duty. She was also very beautiful. From Annie's side, Frederick was fit, attractive and poised at the start of a successful career. While at Margate he published another article which showed his eclectic interests, this time on 'The psychology of general paralysis of the insane' (1876). It helped Annie share Frederick's belief in himself as a budding if not fully-fledged medical genius. In 1877 they were married.

While convinced of his own ability and full of energy to test it, Treves did not have a job. His priorities now were to find one and to study for the Royal College of Surgeons fellowship examination. At this point he was not sure what sort of medicine he wanted to practice. Surgery was only one option among many, and as the article on GPI suggests, he was developing a keen interest in psychology. In the event, he decided to buy a share in the general practice of William Milligan in Wirksworth. The small Derbyshire town seems an unlikely starting point for such a distinguished career, but it was good experience. It also provided some sharp lessons in the competitive and conservative nature of medical practice. Almost immediately

Treves's new colleagues began to resent the pretentiousness of their new partner, with his up-to-date learning and his desire to write. In the end, five events led to a break with them.

The first was his attempted blood transfusion in the case of the woman with pernicious anaemia. The second was his account, published in the *Lancet*, of a gruesome quarry accident. The article, on 'The functions of the frontal lobes of the brain, as illustrated by a case of injury' (1878), described a case in which a quarry worker was struck on the forehead by a stone (which Treves described as 'about the size of a hen's egg' – the first of many homely similes he would employ in his scientific writing, evidence of the influence of both William Barnes and Jonathan Hutchinson). The patient was sensible and able to walk when Treves arrived on the scene. In describing the wound, Treves reveals another aspect of his writing style, the ability to give precise descriptions in the minutest detail:

> On the forehead there was a clean-cut wound of angular shape, commencing at a point about a quarter of an inch above the middle of the right eyebrow, running inwards parallel to the eyebrow as far as the middle line, and then extending obliquely upwards for about an inch and a half. It exposed a severely comminuted and depressed fracture of the frontal bone, the fragments being driven in a considerable depth.
>
> (Treves 1878)

When Treves removed twenty-six pieces of bone, 'a small portion of brain, about the size of a pea, escaped from the right corner of the wound'. The man remained conscious over the next few days, but eventually a large amount of brain matter escaped and the man died within a week. Treves paid careful attention to his patient's movements throughout, charting them meticulously. He conducted a post-mortem within three hours of death, and published his claim that 'bilateral destruction of the antero-frontal region causes neither motor nor sensory paralysis'.

The third error Treves committed was to publish a six-thousand word essay on 'The physiology of some phases of the poetic mind' in the *Journal of Mental Science* (1878). It is a curious piece in which Treves argues that the poetic imagination is in some sense 'abnormal', refusing to think along ordinary lines and creating unusual connections between apparently unrelated things. While Treves demonstrates his sympathy with the art of poetry, his attempt at a pathology of it is doomed to failure. He cannot locate the 'seat' of poetic power, and in the end he is confined to a celebration of it, and the observation that too much attention to fact (as in much scientific thinking) necessarily dulls the power to create or to enjoy poetry. The choice of subject was beyond the comprehension of his colleagues.

The fourth event which hastened Treves's departure was the fact that he passed his fellowship examinations on his first attempt in 1870 at the very young age of twenty-five – a feat that astonished his senior partners. But the final straw came when a lady of high social standing in Wirksworth specifically requested that Treves should deliver the child she was expecting shortly. Milligan was incensed at this, claiming that it was his duty to attend at such an important birth. Treves retorted that it was the patient who had the right to choose. Milligan and his partners conferred and decided that the patient's wishes should be overruled. Treves had had enough of the jealousy and pettiness of his partners. His career in general practice was over at twenty-five. He and Annie packed their bags and took the next train to London.

*   *   *

While happy to be back in London's more sophisticated and cosmopolitan environment, the Treveses had to face that fact that Frederick was now unemployed. His first port of call was the London. He was offered the lowly post of surgical registrar, with its long hours and bad pay. He took it and found rooms at 31 King Edward's Road in South Hackney – an address from which Harley Street seemed very distant indeed.

Because the surgical registrar's post was so badly paid, Treves also worked as a demonstrator in physiology at the London, and as a clinical assistant at the Royal London Orthopaedic Hospital. The half-occupied days of Margate and Wirksworth were a thing of the past. From now on, Treves would do the work of two men to advance his career. He imposed a rigid discipline upon himself, and would continue to do so until he retired.

For Treves his junior appointments were more than simply *rites de passage* preceding a comfortable, professional middle age. They were periods of apprenticeship in which he set himself the dual task of perfecting surgical and anatomical knowledge and technique as well as developing a highly individual method of teaching and writing. It was particularly as a demonstrator in physiology – not really his subject – that Treves's unique ability to communicate with students first manifested itself. While he himself had a sharp academic brain, he realized that this quality was rare among medical students. Whereas the often unruly young doctors of the London would taunt the pretentiously scholarly members of the teaching staff, Treves's rugged good looks and his interest in games combined well with his intellect to make him attractive to all his students. By pitching his style of teaching at the average student he took most of his class with him, leaving the bottom ranks with the feeling that they too could achieve good results, while not alienating the high fliers. A populist rather than a pedant, Treves mixed with his students socially and played games with them. During his first year as a teacher he founded the students' union, and was responsible for setting up an extramural sports programme with other schools which still exists today.

The reasons why the London appealed to Treves as a place to work are the same that made him choose it as a student: volume and variety of surgical cases, and the quality of some of the staff. After the small-mindedness of his Wirksworth partners, Treves was elated to find himself working side by side as a colleague with Jonathan Hutchinson, who was then at the forefront of research into syphilis. He also learned a great deal from the surgeon Jeremiah McCarthy, an expert on cholera.

In September 1879, after less than a year at the London, Treves was promoted to assistant surgeon. By 1880 he was a demonstrator in anatomy and a lecturer in practical anatomy. As soon as his salary increased, he abandoned his rooms in Hackney and moved to a more salubrious – though somewhat Bohemian – address at number 18 Gordon Square in Bloomsbury. By now a young surgeon of twenty-seven might well have been thinking of making his next move. But Treves had thrown himself wholeheartedly into the life of the London, and gambled on the hospital meeting his needs. And he needed constant promotion and success in order to satisfy not only his social and professional ambition, but something much deeper within his character: a drive for excess, that demanded he do as many things as possible as well as possible.

In 1880 we get an inkling of a central aspect of Treves's character: the desire to reform. It is something that identifies him at every stage of his life and in every sphere in which he had influence. At the practical level of the surgeon, he was always seeking new methods and new tools. At the administrative and political level he was always looking for new ways to organize for maximum efficiency – as he would in his reform of the Royal Army Medical Corps after the Boer War. The first evidence of this urge to reform may be found in a letter to the *Lancet*. (It is worth noting that Treves generally preferred to communicate via the *Lancet* as opposed to the *British Medical Journal* – the *Lancet* being a more liberal publication, having distinguished itself by objecting to the iniquities of the Anatomy Act in 1832 and often siding against medical abuses.) The letter concerned the problem of registration of diseases in hospitals, which he considered to be haphazard and inaccurate. The solution he put forward would help the epidemiologists who charted the movement of disease across the country, simplify administration and further the education of students. Treves argued that registrars were too busy to take notes at first hand and generally presented a second-hand report. Why not train students to take accurate notes? This would sharpen their observational and descriptive abilities and make better use of the registrar's time. To the objection that students would require a certain amount of supervision which might negate the proposed saving in time, Treves argued:

> Where any defects were observed in the notes, the first difficulty was to communicate the fact to the dresser, who probably was not on the spot. This difficulty was easily overcome by the use of slips of conspicuous red paper, with a printed heading stating their source, and upon these slips any defects in the notes were written. These slips affixed to the bed-board were too conspicuous to be overlooked by the dresser, who on seeing the case would correct the defect in the manner advised. This plan I found answered very well, and would enable a registrar to compile notes upon any arranged plan.
>
> (Treves 1880)

This eminently practical proposal for reform also reveals another aspect of Treves's character. It was not devised by Treves, but by his (unnamed) predecessor. Nowhere does Treves claim credit for the idea. But it was his name that was attached to the letter read by thousands of his colleagues, and the proposal was from then on associated with him. Later in his career, Treves was to face conflicts of priority, particularly in the case of the diagnosis and operative treatment of appendicitis. Other medical men attempted to gain the notice of the King and the War Office in an effort to plan the reform of the RAMC, but Treves won out. Even where all other things were equal, Treves generally succeeded where his competitors failed because of his natural ability for public relations and his willingness to fight. The shy boy who hid in the cupboard at William Barnes's school had disappeared a long time before.

In 1881 Treves showed the world why he was destined to become the most famous surgeon of his generation. He published ten articles in medical journals on a range of subjects, but especially on severe abnormalities. These articles generally appeared in the *Transactions of the Pathological Society of London*, and what they lacked in a wider readership they made up for in horror. Usually accompanied by his own fine drawings, the articles in 1881 focused on osteitis deformans, a villous polyp of the bladder, a dissection of a congenital hydrocele of the neck (particularly gruesome) and a description of a vesical calculus from a dog. Treves earned a reputation for riveting presentations of this material at meetings of the society.

In 1881 he was elected Erasmus Wilson Professor of Pathology – an extraordinary achievement for a young man of twenty-eight. During the year of his professorship he was required to give a lecture to the Royal College of Surgeons. Resurrecting the scrofula research he did during his summer in Margate, he lectured on the pathology of scrofulus lymphatic glands. In 1882 it was published as *Scrofula and Its Gland Diseases* and was an immediate success, with two American editions appearing in quick succession. The *Lancet* reviewer said: 'the author may be considered as entering a new country, and describing for the first time its general aspect and territorial limits'.

It is worth dwelling on the problem of scrofula because it reveals a great deal about surgery's transition from craft to science, about the speed with which established medical *belief* was being superseded by *knowledge* and about Treves's use of history as an element of contemporary practice. In the opening pages of his book, Treves eschews the arrogance of much scientific writing of the period and admits that 'the scientific outlines of the disease, called scrofula, are blurred and indistinct . . . unless a precise definition can be given, the term "scrofula" becomes almost an untranslatable word, having a meaning only for the individual who uses it'. The term was also difficult because it was the subject of a popular mythology. It had always been known in England as the 'King's evil', because it was believed that the touch of the monarch could cure it. The power of this belief over rationality may be judged by the fact that Dr Johnson, that paragon of reason, was touched by Queen Anne in 1712.

Scrofula later came to be understood as a tubercular abscess of gland or bone discharging onto the surface of the skin through a sinus. It held a particular horror because it appeared on the neck and the sores emitted a highly unpleasant odour. It was disfiguring if untreated, yet until the development of William Knight Treves's operation, the surgical scar was also prominent, causing almost as much revulsion as the condition itself. Scrofula was hardly ever fatal; but its sufferers were stigmatized and ostracized from society.

The fact that very little had been published on scrofula in English (Treves does cite German work, however) helped to determine his approach to medical writing. With almost no literature to fall back on, Treves could create his own method, his own analysis: his own tradition. Where other writers would be discouraged by a lack of prior research, Treves took the opportunity to proclaim:

> the greater part of the material in this volume is the result of my own investigations into this disease. The clinical facts I have detailed are drawn from a careful examination of a very large number of scrofulous persons, and in such examination I have endeavoured to proceed free from the bias of any preconceived ideas.
>
> (Treves 1882)

He argued that scrofula was a tendency towards inflammation and that the tubercle present in scrofula was an immature version of that found in tuberculosis. The difference between scrofula and tuberculosis then was one of degree rather than kind.

By one of those coincidences which are the bane of the scientific researcher, the German bacteriologist Robert Koch was completing his research into the subject just as Treves was preparing his final draft for press. By discovering the tubercle bacillus, Koch had solved the scrofula problem. Treves's book became history almost as soon as it appeared. He was philosophical about this turn of events, and thirteen years later he used the episode to reflect on how the concept of scrofula highlighted a particularly negative aspect of medical thinking – a preoccupation with blustering discourse which had nothing to do with the problem at hand or with science:

> Scrofula was in every way a convenient disorder. It was a cloak

which covered a multitude of pathological sins. It represented something in the blood; it had a whispered relationship to syphilis; there was about it something of the attractive romance which attaches to an obscure domestic scandal. In reality the term stood, like the algebraical x, as representative of a profound quality of ignorance. There was little agreement as to what scrofula really was, except to the extent that it admitted a large factor of the unknown. As soon as the term 'tubercle' crept into existence scrofula and tuberculosis began to play the part of two Dromios in a tedious Comedy of Errors. Among the minor benefits which mark the close of the nineteenth century must be placed the discovery which brought this drama to an end. Nothing in the literature of medicine can compare with the great war of words which waged around these two time-worn terms.

(Treves 1895)

From 1882 Treves's medical career steams ahead at a breathtaking pace. What is remarkable is not only the volume of work he produces, but the variety of it: in surgical technique, in social medicine and in anatomy. His first real contribution to surgical technique involved the rather unpleasant operation of excision of the entire tongue. At that time a controversy raged between two methods, Billroth's and Whitehead's. Both advocated quick excision by means of scissors, but Billroth practised deligation of the two lingual arteries in the neck. Through careful presentation of surgical cases, Treves resolved the debate by showing that risk of haemorrhage was greatly reduced by Billroth's method.

Far more importantly, he addressed the problem of how one dealt with reuniting portions of intestine. Two options were open to the surgeon: creating an artificial anus, or reuniting by suture. Clearly the latter option was preferable to the patient, but certain problems attached to the operation. It was difficult to hold the ends of the intestine in place while suturing, a situation compounded by the fact that the two ends were of unequal size. The other problem was that an uneven suture line could lead to leakage of intestinal material, which would be fatal. Treves's solution was to invent a device which had two parts. The first was a pair of clamps which held each end of the gut. These were joined by transverse bars so that a square frame was formed, holding the parts in place. The second was a small rubber bag which the surgeon would insert into either end of the intestine. When

24

pumped with air it would dilate each part to an equal size, allowing the surgeon to suture neatly and evenly. Before the last two sutures were introduced, the bag would be deflated and withdrawn, and the operation completed. While an ingenious concept, the apparatus proved unsuccessful.

Treves's forays into social medicine were concerned with the health of workers in a local match factory and with dress and its relation to health. A letter to the *Lancet* drew attention to the fact that cases of phosphorous necrosis (a disease which affects the maxilla, the facial bone which helps form the upper jaw) were appearing in London. Treves himself had treated three cases of phosphorous necrosis in six months. He pointed out that it was a common (but mistaken) belief among employers that those with sound teeth and jaws were immune to the disease. Treves's three cases all had sound teeth and jaws before taking up jobs in a local match factory, of which there were a number near the London. Each of the patients had been given a dental examination before starting work, but no follow-up checks were ever carried out. Treves used the rhetoric of science rather than politics to argue the case of these victims of industrial disease. He said that without regular dental inspection of workers, the employers' assumptions about it only affecting those with unsound teeth and jaws should be viewed with suspicion.

In his essay *The Dress of the Period in its Relation to Health* (1882), Treves joined a long line of doctors who pronounced on the 'unhealthiness' of female fashion. He had a curious fascination for clothes, and his travel books are full of vivid and usually disparaging descriptions of them, from frilly dresses on Brighton ladies to loincloths on African natives. The essay on dress is unintentionally hilarious to the modern reader, but the author was deadly serious when he declared that pointed shoes, high heels and corsets all presented a threat to the health of the nation: 'Let all those, therefore, who practise tight-lacing (if even to a slight extent) distinctly understand that the narrowing of the waist is effected mainly at the expense of the internal organs.'

Treves's professional triumphs of 1882 were eclipsed by the birth of a daughter, Hetty. It was a moment of great joy, coming at a time when his career was well launched and he was beginning to earn a modest amount of fame in the profession. Hetty was soon followed by Enid – the last child to be born to Frederick and Annie. The timing of the births shows the caution Treves inherited from his father and grandfather. He had planned his life, and things were going according to plan.

Treves owed his success to a strictly regimented personal schedule which he observed faithfully. He rose each morning at six and wrote for two hours. He was a fast writer, and most of his manuscripts required little editing. His travel books were printed more or less as they arrived on the publisher's desk: in a neat, copperplate hand and an easy, flowing style. Friends and colleagues were constantly astonished at his vast output of writing. But Treves would always argue that a two hour stint of writing every morning was more than most professional authors (he always considered himself an amateur) achieved. Two thousand words a day equals a minimum of ten thousand words a week equals the possibility of half a million words a year. . . .

At eight he took breakfast and read his correspondence. The morning was spent teaching and doing surgical rounds at the London. He often made time for students over lunch, offering encouragement and taking a genuine interest in their lives apart from the hospital. The afternoon was spent operating at the London or seeing private patients. He would arrive home at five or six in the evening and spend time with Annie and the girls until dinner, when he devoted himself entirely to his wife. The Treveses did not entertain much at home. His early success, unlike that of some of his colleagues, was due entirely to his performance as a researcher, teacher and surgeon rather than to the cultivation of influence over the dinner table. (Treves always tried to restrict his dining out to once a week, usually after giving a paper to one of the medical societies or attending a meeting of one of the many committees on which he served.) After dinner he would correct proofs of books or articles, or prepare a lecture for the next day. He was usually in bed by ten o'clock.

While the critics were enthusing over his successes of 1882, Treves was not resting on his laurels. He organized all of the knowledge he had amassed as a teacher of anatomy at the London and published *Surgical Applied Anatomy* (1883) – one of the most enduring medical textbooks of modern times, the last edition of which appeared in 1962. Its premise was the basis of all Treves's teaching: 'to assist the student in judging the comparative value to him, when applying it practically, of the anatomy he had learnt by attending lectures and dissecting and to show him how to encourage the survival of the fittest of the many hard and unassimilable facts he had then acquired.' While Treves himself could be described as an intellectual – his bibliography supports that claim – he was, in fact, a teacher who encouraged average students to discover what was essential for their own purposes and to apply that knowledge well. For this reason, *Surgical Applied Anatomy* is probably Treves's most important contribution as a writer on surgery. Reviewing the 1962 edition, Norman C. Lake wrote:

> there is much to praise and little to criticize in the present volume. . . . A book which was first published seventy-nine years ago and which has reached its fourteenth edition, with numerous reprintings, must clearly have great merit. If at the same time it has managed to preserve its primary form while being revised and brought up to date in succeeding editions, its original author should be credited with exceptional foresight.
>
> (Lake 1962)

Treves's success did much to enhance the standing of the London Hospital medical school. Students began to flock not just from the remoter provinces of Britain, but from round the world. Already, Treves was taking his place as an equal alongside such luminaries as Hutchinson and Jackson. But success also brought with it the jealousy of colleagues and some difficult relations within the hospital. Walter Rivington, whose history of medicine had influenced him, already had a reputation as a less than brilliant surgeon. Increasingly students noted the difference in ability between Rivington and his younger colleague. One of Treves's students at the time, A. T. Schofield, scornfully dismisses Rivington in his memoirs as 'a trifling "absent-minded beggar"'. He cites the example of:

> one afternoon, when he had a number of operations, one being under chloroform already in the theatre, another being anaesthetised, and several others waiting their turn, he was found to be missing; he was nowhere in the Hospital, but an out-patient, coming in, reported he had met him walking down the Whitechapel Road. A fleet-footed student caught him up, serenely walking home to Harley Street under the impression that the day's work was finished.
>
> (Schofield)

By contrast Treves was viewed with both respect and affection by most students. They admired his teaching style as well as his personal manner: his precise mind and his sharp tongue. An anonymous student recalled:

> Treves was of a nature very precise. His habit of mind was to reduce all subjects to headings, duly numbered, with the result that he often missed the delicate side of things. Nevertheless, this sense of extreme order made him one of the best teachers a medical student could have. He was therefore followed in the wards by a vast crowd, and every case made simple for the ordinary mind. With his operations he was the same – a clear exposition at first, followed by a complete success. His method of teaching was rendered more attractive by a constant flow of sarcasm directed against his dressers or even his house surgeon.
>
> (Schofield)

Though he was fond of his students, Treves did not spare them a tongue lashing. Wilfred Grenfell recalls how Treves

> on one occasion asking a dresser for his diagnosis, the student replied: 'It might be a fracture, sir, or it might be only sprained.' 'The patient is not interested to know that it might be measles, or it might be toothache. The patient wants to know what is the matter, and it is your business to tell it to him or he will go to a quack who will inform him at once.'
>
> (Grenfell 1922)

He was also given to 'racy' descriptions in his teaching of anatomy. W. R. Bett offers a mild example:

> It was in our anatomy days that the name of Treves first came to our ear. Were we not constantly reminded by one of the least pornographic mnemonics of our youth that 'Treves is an excellent surgeon, especially in peritonitis,' or 'except in piles'? The slight variation depended upon the school in which we were trained or upon personal tastes.
>
> (Bett 1953)

Treves's sarcasm was not confined to the wards and the operating theatre, and he was given to public comment on those whom he judged pretentious or incompetent. Schofield recalls, 'I remember on one occasion asking him his opinion of the greatest surgeon of another hospital. "He is a man," said Treves, "of microscopic intellect, delirious with a sense of his own importance"'. On the other hand, he could be infinitely tolerant of the behaviour of the ordinary people who passed through the London as patients; for example, here is Grenfell's account of his teacher's encounter with a Whitechapel prostitute suffering from violent delirium tremens, who

> was lying screeching in a strait-jacket on the cushioned floor of the padded room. With the usual huge queue of students following, he had gone in to see her, as I had been unable to get the results desired with a reasonable quantity of sedatives and soporifics. It was a very rare occasion, for cases which did not involve active surgery he left strictly alone. After giving a talk on psychical influence he had the jacket removed as 'a relic of barbarism', and in a very impressive way, looking into her glaring eyes and shaking his forefinger at her, he said: 'Now, you are comfortable, my good woman, and will sleep. You will make no more disturbance whatever.' There was an unusual silence. The woman remained absolutely passive, and we all turned to follow the chief out. Suddenly the 'lady' called out, 'Hi, hi' – and some perverse spirit induced Sir Frederick to return. Looking back with defiant eyes she screamed out, 'You! You with a faice! You do think yourself ... clever, don't yer?' The strange situation was only relieved by his bursting into a genuine fit of laughter.
>
> (Schofield)

While in 1883 *Surgical Applied Anatomy* was helping to lead surgery into the modern age, the reality of Treves's operating theatre belonged to another period. Bertrand Dawson (later Lord Dawson of Penn) was one of Treves's students from 1882, and was destined to achieve even greater fame than his master as a court surgeon (not least in our time for the revelation that he administered a lethal injection to King George VI, who decided that euthanasia was preferable to a lingering death). When Dawson first watched Treves operating, he wore 'an old and well-worn coat which, as he once boasted to Ernest Morris, "was so stiff with congealed blood after many years of use that it would stand upright when placed on the floor"' (Watson 1950). Lister's teaching had no practical effect at the London until the 1890s. E. C. Montgomery-Smith, a student then, describes the change which had occurred.

The first operation I ever saw was in Treves's theatre, when he

29

amputated a man's leg above the knee. At this time *bacteria* had only just been discovered and by no means all surgeons believed in their existence. Treves invariably changed into a white coat and scrubbed his hands meticulously before operating, but a man who was in charge of the instruments and threaded the needles, sometimes sucked the thread before inserting it in the needles, and handed them to Treves.

(Montgomery-Smith 1961)

At the end of 1883 Treves's diligence was rewarded when he succeeded Walter Rivington as head of the anatomy school; in 1884 he was appointed full surgeon to the London. In the years that followed Treves continued his astonishing output of books and articles on every aspect of surgery, including *The Anatomy of the Intestinal Canal and Peritoneum in Man* (1885) and the three-volume *A Manual of Surgery* (1886). In 1886 he further enhanced his reputation with students by calling for an MD degree for the London universities. At that time, they did not offer one, and as a consequence, many students began to choose Irish, Scottish and continental universities to the detriment of the London teaching hospitals. In the end, Treves's suggestion was taken up.

In 1887 Treves realized his ambition of reaching the top of his profession. At thirty-four, he moved his family to an elegant Georgian house at number 34 Wimpole Street. Here he lived in style, and would soon command the highest fees of any London surgeon. He and Annie could look back at their impoverished Hackney life with relief and good humour. Freddie had arrived.

But later that year Treves found himself back in Hackney, under the influence of two favourite students: Wilfred Grenfell and D. G. Halsted. Grenfell was a particularly undistinguished student academically, but Treves admired his energy, and was sympathetic to the muscular Christianity which inspired him to start a mission at St Jude's Episcopal Church at Bethnal Green which eventually became the Boy's Brigade.

Grenfell and Halsted lived in a rented house in Palestine Place in Hackney. They were keen athletes and had the idea that sport could be the attraction that would lure the tough East End boys off the streets and into a Christian mission. They converted the ground floor of their house into a small gymnasium where they taught boxing and gymnastics. Treves was brought in as the first president of the Boy's

Brigade. He took an active interest in the project and helped his students find ways to expand their activities. All three men shared a love of sailing – Treves and Grenfell jointly owned a small yawl, *The Vagabond* – and many of the boys learned to sail her round Lulworth Cove, where Treves had bought a house. Despite his frantic schedule, Treves attended Boy's Brigade summer camps, teaching swimming and sailing. He even contributed articles to *Boy's Own Paper*.

Treves's fondness for Grenfell played a decisive role in the younger man's later career as England's most famous medical missionary. Indeed, had it not been for Treves, Grenfell would probably never have become Grenfell of Labrador. That story begins with the founding of the Royal National Mission to Deep Sea Fishermen in 1881. In 1882 Treves became its honorary surgeon and chairman of the medical section. (In 1907, after his retirement, he became its chairman.) When the mission was founded, North Sea fishermen worked two-month shifts on small sailing smacks. It was difficult and dangerous work and many fishermen were injured, especially during the transfer at sea of the smaller boats' catches to larger carriers. There were no ship's doctors then, and not much training in first aid. Injured fishermen were transferred to the carriers and brought to Billingsgate, which meant that they ended up on Treves's wards at the London. Treves advised the mission on the fitting out of hospital ships, and was then asked if he could recommend young doctors who might be interested (and fit) enough to endure a poorly paid two-month tour of duty on a fishing smack in the depths of winter. He immediately thought of Grenfell, who signed up for a stint on board the *Thomas Grey*. To this modest beginning are owed the hospitals, orphanages and nursing stations which Grenfell later established along the Newfoundland and Labrador coasts.

Treves's other favourite student at this time was Henry Tonks, the painter and teacher of art who started life as a surgeon. Tonks was highly qualified at a very young age, having already obtained his membership of the Royal College of Surgeons when he came to the London as Treves's house surgeon in 1887, aged twenty-five. Treves considered him the most brilliant student of his year. They struck up a close friendship and Tonks was often a guest – a privilege rarely accorded – at Treves's house in Wimpole Street. When Tonks's stint as a dresser had finished, Treves was instrumental in getting him a place as senior medical officer at the Royal Free Hospital.

It is hard to imagine two more different personalities than Tonks and Grenfell. Each highlights an aspect of Treves's character, and each is curiously complementary. Grenfell was a poor student but an energetic and caring doctor; Tonks was a brilliant student and was not very interested in treating patients. Treves himself thought that Tonks did not have the temperament of a surgeon, and Tonks's biographer Joseph Hone confirms this.

> Once while he was entertaining some friends at the Royal Free Hospital, the porter came in to say that a man was below with a bad head wound. 'Please sir, a man with a cut 'ead.' Tonks was annoyed and said, as he went on carving the chicken, 'Cut off his hair.' The answer was: 'Please sir, I 'ave done.' Tonks became enraged, and raising his carving knife high above his head, he plunged it into the table, and left the room shouting: 'Damn the man, cut off his head.'
>
> (Hone 1939)

By 1892 Tonks began to suspect that the life of a surgeon was not for him. When he was offered a job teaching art at the Slade School, he knew he should accept. Even though he had made his mind up, he spent many hours debating the pros and cons with Treves. It was some consolation to Tonks to be able to tell his family that, all things considered, the great Frederick Treves thought his decision a good one.

By now Treves's fame as a surgeon was already assured. But he had no inkling of just how famous he would become through his connection with the royal family, starting with his appointment as surgeon in ordinary to the Duke of York in 1897. In fact, this appointment might have come earlier had it not been for a comedy of errors which prevented him meeting the Queen in the early 1880s when the Royal National Mission to Deep Sea Fishermen launched the first hospital ship equipped to Treves's specifications, *The Queen Victoria*. When the ship was ready, the Queen asked if it could be brought from Yarmouth to Cowes for her to inspect. The secretary of the mission asked Treves's colleague A. T. Schofield if he would conduct the tour. Schofield agreed and took the five a.m. train to Southampton, where he was joined by the secretary to the mission and an illustrator from one of the London magazines who was dressed in a dapper outfit of cap, muffler, frock coat and slippers. Schofield described the illustrator as 'even at that early hour, somewhat exhilarated'. A royal launch awaited the inspection party, and Schofield's first job was to place the illustrator in the care of a Captain Goldsmid. Goldsmid handed the tipsy artist over to one of his men with strict instructions that he be placed in a boat and rowed about well away from the Queen until the inspection was over. Schofield then describes what happened when he and the secretary were taken to the Queen's yard at East Cowes:

Captain Goldsmid very naturally asked the secretary whereabouts the Hospital Ship was lying. The secretary, however, did not know. The boat had been ordered to Cowes, and he presumed she was there.

'How do you expect to find her?' inquired the captain.

The secretary again did not know, so when we had reported by telephone to Sir Henry Ponsonby at Osborne House that we had arrived, Captain Goldsmid asked what we proposed to do. Seeing clearly that we still did not know, he very kindly came to the rescue, and sent a boat up the River Medina, the launch into the Roads, and the yacht *Elfin* down the Solent to hunt for the missing boat. In half an hour they all came back saying that *The Queen Victoria* could not be found. By this time the secretary very naturally had got almost frantic, as Captain Goldsmid explained to him that the Queen expected to inspect the Hospital Ship at eleven o'clock.

Eventually we had to tell our dreadful plight to Sir Henry Ponsonby, who, after telephoning Portsmouth, at last sent us the joyful news that Sir Edmund Commerell had found the boat and was sending *The Queen Victoria* to Osborne Bay in charge of an Admiralty tug. Our launch, with a small boat in tow, was then brought round, and away we went to the bay to meet our ship. On the shore were the Empress of Germany and her two daughters, violently waving their parasols to our boat. So we sent a sailor with the dinghy to the shore to bring them to the launch; but just as the Empress was stepping into the boat, two equerries galloped up and spoke to her. The boat came back with the message that the Queen had (doubtless under advice) postponed the inspection till the next day. We now turned our eyes to Portsmouth, and there was the fussy tug with *The Queen Victoria* – a most gruesome sight – behind her. The topmast was hanging over the side, bulwarks were shattered and the ship a wreck. We found she had been caught in a gale, and had been lying in Portsmouth to refit for four days. We towed her to

Cowes and put the fear of the Queen into the hearts of the shipbuilders to such purpose that at eleven o'clock the next morning she was at Osborne Bay all spick and span.

To attend to my practice perforce I returned to town, and in my place Sir Frederick Treves went down the next day to Portsmouth. Being told there by wire he must cross by an Admiralty tug to Osborne, he got over to Gosport with some difficulty, and eventually arrived at the Admiralty Yard.

'What name?' said the Orderly in waiting, and his card was sent in to Sir Edmund Commerell, and he was told to enter. With some difficulty Sir Frederick explained he wanted an Admiralty tug to take him to Osborne Bay. Sir Edmund, very much irritated by the events of the day before, became very indignant.

'We have no tugs for private gentlemen,' he said, 'you should have crossed by the Ryde steamer.'

'But it's just gone,' said Treves meekly.

'Well, you've a chance still,' said Sir Edmund. 'The Queen's yacht *Elfin* is at the Victualling Yard, and will take you straight across if you hurry up.'

So Sir Frederick dashed off into the rain and arrived in a state of exhaustion only to see the *Elfin* just leaving her berth. There being no hope in this quarter, he in despair returned to the Admiralty Yard, and, undeterred by some uncomplimentary remarks from Sir Edmund which he overheard when his name was sent in, once more declared 'he must be transported to Osborne Bay by the Queen's orders'. Unable to swim or fly, he 'looked to Sir Edmund to transport him'. This gentleman at last, though himself transported with rage, telephoned up and down for a torpedo boat. But alas! none had steam up, and his final advice to Sir Frederick was to go to the George Hotel, and get the best breakfast he could, and take the first train back to London; which he did; and no one but the secretary showed the Queen and the Prince of Wales over the Hospital Ship.

(Schofield)

So Treves's first encounter with the Queen and future King of England was delayed by nearly a decade.

Chapter Four

MONSTERS

Treves's work as an anatomist led to an interest in pathology – the causes and effects of diseases. He was particularly fascinated by very unusual cases of deformity and disease, and between 1880 and 1898 he was a regular speaker at meetings of the Pathological Society of London.

The first case of gross deformity which Treves presented was a living specimen of osteitis deformans or Paget's disease in 1880 – a chronic disease of the skeleton in which there is softening of the bone followed by a thickening of the cortex. In 1881 he presented a dissection of a congenital hydrocele of the neck in a male child who died in his third week. In three weeks the tumour grew in proportion to the rest of the child's body, measuring eight by six inches against the child's height of only nineteen and a half inches. In 1882 he described a most unusual case titled 'Congenital coccygeal tumour: attached foetus'. The specimen was an infant born with a bizarre tumour which had the appearance of a head, was covered with fine hair and had five appendages (one of which had a primitive motor function). And in November 1883 he presented a congenital malformation in which the skull of an infant who had only lived twelve hours was represented by a thin membrane.

These gruesome displays of nature gone wrong were usually descriptive; they did not generally involve a diagnosis. While they did not add much to the canon of medical knowledge – they were often unsolved mysteries – they were good for Treves's career, and he developed a reputation for 'discovering' more unusual cases than anyone else. In 1884, however, he attempted a diagnosis of a living case which he got wrong. On 4 January he presented a patient 'who presented a series of peculiar ulcerations and growths, extending from the neck and jaw obliquely across the chest. The uppermost growth was traversed by a sinus leading down to the lower jaw; in the posterior triangle of the neck was a deep excavation, filled with a cheesy-looking material.' The case had come to Treves via his brother William in Margate. Together they arrived at a diagnosis of actinomycosis, because the case seemed almost identical to those described by Ponfinck of Breslau. It was a very unusual diagnosis because actinomycosis usually occurred in cattle. Discovered by Bollinger of Munich in 1877, it is a chronic inflammation caused by the actinomyces or ray fungus. The main symptom in cattle is a lumpy jaw. In 1879 Ponfinck performed a post-mortem on a man presenting fistulous openings on the skin of the neck, and found the same sulphur-yellow bodies discovered by Bollinger in cattle. Very few cases of the disease had been identified in man; Treves's would have been the first ever in Britain.

Treves viewed the case as another opportunity to be first, to make a discovery, to promote his career. However, he cautiously titled his paper 'A supposed case of actinomycosis'. It received more space than was usual in the *Transactions* and aroused a great deal of interest. Treves then performed two operations on the patient. In the first he successfully removed large portions of the growths around his neck and jaw. After the second operation, to remove growths at the back of the neck and elsewhere, the patient made an initial recovery, but began to bleed profusely on the second day. A few days later he died.

A post-mortem revealed that Treves's diagnosis had been wrong. No micro-organisms were found. In a second presentation of the case in May he had to admit his error, leaving the condition undiagnosed. He described the tumour vaguely as a large-celled sarcoma 'of a peculiar type'. While Treves's first medical paper on a failed attempt at transfusion underlined the value of medical failure as well as success, he increasingly preferred success. Later in 1884 he would find his greatest pathological 'success' in Joseph Merrick, the so-called Elephant Man.

Treves first met Merrick at a freak show run by a back-street entrepreneur by the name of Tom Norman. Norman was showing the Elephant Man at the rear of a vacant waxworks (which contained gruesome models of Jack the Ripper's victims) opposite the London Hospital in Whitechapel Road. The great pathologist John Bland-Sutton had already seen Merrick. Treves learned of him from his house surgeon, Reginald Tuckett. In *The Elephant Man and Other Reminiscences*, Treves describes his reaction upon first seeing Merrick:

The showman – speaking as if to a dog – called out harshly: 'Stand up!' The thing arose slowly and let the blanket that covered its head and back fall to the ground. There stood revealed the most disgusting specimen of humanity that I have ever seen. In the course of my profession I had come upon lamentable deformities of the face due to injury or disease, as well as mutilations and contortions of the body depending upon like causes; but at no time had I met with such a degraded or perverted version of a human being as this lone figure displayed. He was naked to the waist, his feet were bare, he wore a pair of threadbare trousers that had once belonged to some fat gentleman's suit.

From the intensified painting in the street I had imagined the Elephant Man to be of gigantic size. This, however, was a little man below the average height and made to look shorter by the bowing of his back. The most striking feature about him was his enormous and misshapen head. From the brow there projected a huge bony mass like a loaf, while from the back of the head hung a bag of spongy, fungous-looking skin the surface of which was comparable to brown cauliflower. On the top of the skull were a few long lank hairs. The osseous growth on the forehead almost occluded one eye. The circumference of the head was no less than that of the man's waist. From the upper jaw there projected another mass of bone. It protruded from the mouth like a pink stump, turning the upper lip inside out and making of the mouth a mere slobbering aperture. This growth from the jaw had been so exaggerated in the painting as to appear to be a rudimentary trunk or tusk. The nose was merely a lump of flesh, only recognizable as a nose from its position. The face was no more capable of expression than a block of gnarled wood. The back was horrible, because from it hung, as far down as the middle of the thigh, huge, sack-like masses of flesh covered by the same loathsome cauliflower skin.

The right arm was of enormous size and shapeless. It suggested the limb of the subject of elephantiasis. It was overgrown also with pendent masses of the same cauliflower-like skin. The hand was large and clumsy – a fin or paddle rather than a hand. There was no distinction between the palm and the back. The thumb had the appearance of a radish, while the fingers might have been thick, tuberous roots. As a limb it was almost useless. The other arm was remarkable by contrast. It was not only normal but was, moreover, a delicately shaped limb covered with fine skin and provided with a beautiful hand which any woman might have envied. From the chest hung a bag of the same repulsive flesh. It was like a dewlap suspended from the neck of a lizard. The lower limbs had the characters of the deformed arm. They were unwieldy, dropsical looking and grossly misshapened.

To add a further burden to his trouble the wretched man, when a boy, developed hip disease, which had left him permanently lame, so that he could only walk with a stick. He was thus denied all means of escape from his tormentors. As he told me later, he could never run away. One other feature must be mentioned to emphasize his isolation from his kind. Although he was already repellent enough, there arose from the fungous skin-growth with which he was almost covered a very sickening stench which was hard to tolerate. From the showman I learnt nothing about the Elephant Man, except that he was English, that his name was John Merrick and that he was twenty-one years of age.

(Treves 1923)

Treves's description contains one delicate omission and a glaring error. He neglects to mention that in addition to one perfect arm, Merrick's sex organs were also perfect; and he gets Merrick's Christian name wrong. Treves and Bland-Sutton always referred to him as John; yet his birth certificate shows him to be Joseph, and others at the London later knew him by that name.

Being much more of an opportunist than Bland-Sutton, Treves immediately recognized his next presentation to the Pathological Society. He struck a bargain with Tom Norman and arranged for Merrick to come to the London to be examined. 'To ensure his immediate admission to the college,' Treves wrote, 'I gave him my card. This card was destined to play a critical part in Merrick's life.'

Because of his deformities, Merrick only ventured out of doors dressed in a costume which, though intended to hide his deformities, was of such extraordinary proportion and design that, had he been perfectly normal beneath it, he would still have excited unwanted attention:

> It consisted of a long black cloak which reached to the ground. Whence the cloak had been obtained I cannot imagine. I had only seen such a garment on the stage wrapped about the figure of a Venetian bravo. The recluse was provided with a pair of bag-like slippers in which to hide his deformed feet. On his head was a cap of a kind that was never before seen. It was black like the cloak, had a wide peak, and the general outline of a yachting cap. As the circumference of Merrick's head was that of a man's waist, the size of this headgear may be imagined. From the attachment of the peak a grey flannel curtain hung in front of the face. In this mask was cut a wide horizontal slit through which the wearer could look out. This costume, worn by a bent man hobbling along with a stick, is probably the most remarkable and the most uncanny that has as yet been designed.
>
> (Treves 1923)

Merrick went to the London and Treves made his examination. He touched, prodded, measured, said nothing. He assumed his subject – or object – to be an idiot. When he finished his examination he photographed Merrick, and gave him one of the prints. It would turn up later on the cover of a leaflet which Norman had printed as Merrick's 'autobiography' – a fanciful account which was sold as a freak show programme.

On 2 December Treves was down to present a paper to the Pathological Society on 'Two cases of primary tumour of the soft palate'. When he had finished, he surprised his audience by hijacking the rest of the evening with an unscheduled description of Merrick. Some of those present viewed the event with disgust. Treves's 'great discovery' received only a brief mention in the abstracts section of the *British Medical Journal*. The *Lancet* showed its feeling by giving a full account of the rest of the evening, but leaving out Treves's surprise presentation.

Undeterred, Treves decided to write a full description of Merrick and present it officially to the society. He did, but he was unable to answer his colleagues' insistent question: what was wrong with Merrick? A diagnosis was attempted by Radcliffe Crocker, a young dermatologist at University College Hospital. After Treves's second presentation of the case, Crocker surmised that Merrick's condition 'must surely be classified as belonging to that rare group of disorders known as *dermatolysis* (a loosened or pendulous condition of the skin) and *pachydermatocoele* (a condition where tumours arise from an overgrowth of the skin)'. In his massive *Diseases of the Skin* (1888) Crocker described Merrick as suffering from fibroma. But Treves and Crocker had overlooked the work of Frederich Daniell von Recklinghausen who gave the first description in England of the disease which then bore his name, but which is now known as neurofibromatosis. It is incurable, and it presented Treves with a dilemma. In *The True History of the Elephant Man* (1980) Howell and Ford remark that there is a concise creed which doctors through the ages have attempted to follow: 'to cure sometimes; to relieve often; to comfort always.' Initially Treves did none of those things. The day after he returned Merrick to Tom Norman's squalid exhibit across the Whitechapel Road the police closed down the show. Merrick and Norman disappeared. Looking back on his second farewell to Merrick, Treves later wrote:

> I supposed that Merrick was imbecile and had been imbecile from birth. The fact that his face was incapable of expression, that his speech was a mere spluttering and his attitude that of one whose mind was void of all emotions and concerns gave grounds for this belief. The conviction was no doubt encouraged by the hope that his intellect was the blank I imagined it to be. That he could appreciate his position was unthinkable. Here was a man in the heyday of youth who was so vilely deformed that everyone he met with confronted him with a look of horror and disgust. He was taken about the country to be exhibited as a monstrosity and an object of loathing. He was shunned like a leper, housed like a wild beast, and got his only view of the world from a peephole in a showman's cart. He was, moreover, lame, had but one available arm, and could hardly make his utterances understood. It was not until I came to know that Merrick was highly intelligent, that he possessed an acute sensibility and – worse than all – a romantic imagination that I realised the overwhelming tragedy of his life.
>
> (Treves 1923)

Merrick arrived in Leicester under the control of the loathsome Norman with three possessions: his life savings of fifty pounds, Treves's card and the photograph taken by the surgeon. But public sentiment and the police conspired to close down the Leicester exhibit. Deciding that Merrick was more trouble than he was worth, Norman cut his losses and sold him to an Austrian who took him to Brussels. After a short time the Austrian also tired of Merrick; what promised to be a great European freak show had proved too repugnant to contintental taste. After stealing his life savings, the Austrian abandoned Merrick in Brussels.

Merrick made his way to Ostend where he was befriended by Mr Wardell Cardew. He then travelled back up the coast to Antwerp where he took a steamer to Harwich. It is difficult to imagine the horror of Merrick's predicament. Apart from the obvious impediments of appearance and speech, he had no language other than English, and no experience of fending for himself. Somehow he managed the crossing and arrived eventually at London's Liverpool Street Station where he nearly caused a riot. The police found him in a distressed state clutching his only remaining possession: Treves's card. Treves later tried to envisage what Merrick's ordeal must have been like:

> The journey may be imagined. Merrick was in his alarming outdoor garb. He would be harried by an eager mob as he hobbled along the quay. They would run ahead to get a look at him. They would lift the hem of his cloak to peep at his body. He would try to hide in the train or in some dark corner of the boat, but never could he be free from that ring of curious eyes or from those whispers of fright and aversion. He had but a few shillings in his pocket and nothing either to eat or drink on the way. A panic-dazed dog with a label on his collar would have received some sympathy and possibly some kindness. Merrick received none.
>
> What was he to do when he reached London? He had not a friend in the world. He knew no more of London than he knew of Peking. How could he find a lodging, or what lodging-house keeper would dream of taking him in? All he wanted was to hide. What he most dreaded were the open street and the gaze of his fellow men. If even he crept into a cellar the horrid eyes and the still more deeply dreaded whispers would follow him to its depths. Was there ever such a homecoming?
>
> At Liverpool Street he was rescued from the crowd by the police and taken into the third-class waiting-room. Here he sank

on the floor in the darkest corner. The police were at a loss what to do with him. They had dealt with strange and mouldy tramps, but never with such an object as this. He could not explain himself. His speech was so maimed that he might as well have spoken in Arabic. He had, however, something with him which he produced with a ray of hope. It was my card.

The card simplified matters. It made it evident that this curious creature had an acquaintance and that the individual must be sent for. A messenger was despatched to the London Hospital which is comparatively near at hand. Fortunately I was in the building and returned at once with the messenger to the station. In the waiting-room I had some difficulty in making a way through the crowd, but there, on the floor in the corner, was Merrick. He looked a mere heap. It seemed as if he had been thrown there like a bundle. He was so huddled up and so helpless looking that he might have had both his arms and his legs broken. He seemed pleased to see me, but he was nearly done. The journey and want of food had reduced him to the last stage of exhaustion. The police kindly helped him to a cab, and I drove him at once to the hospital. He appeared to be content, for he fell asleep almost as soon as he was seated and slept to the journey's end. He never said a word, but seemed to be satisfied that all was well.

In the attics of the hospital was an isolation ward with a single bed. It was used for emergency purposes – for a case of delirium tremens, for a man who had become suddenly insane or for a patient with an undetermined fever. Here the Elephant Man was deposited on a bed, was made comfortable and was supplied with food. I had been guilty of an irregularity in admitting such a case, for the hospital was neither a refuge nor a home for incurables. Chronic cases were not accepted, but only those requiring active treatment. I applied to the sympathetic chairman of the committee, Mr Carr Gomm, who not only was good enough to approve my action but who agreed with me that Merrick must not again be turned out into the world.

(Treves 1923)

Despite Carr Gomm's charitable view in this matter, the London's charter stated specifically that it was not a hospital for incurables, and that it could offer them no shelter. It will be remembered that the

London was still a charity hospital, and that the committee had total power over how the institution was run. Treves argued that if a separate source of funding could be found to keep Merrick at the London, the committee might accept his plan.

> Mr Carr Gomm wrote a letter to *The Times* detailing the circumstances of the refugee and asking for money for his support. So generous is the English public that in a few days – I think in a week – enough money was forthcoming to maintain Merrick for life without any charge upon the hospital funds. There chanced to be two empty rooms at the back of the hospital which were little used. They were on the ground floor, were out of the way, and opened upon a large courtyard called Bedstead Square, because the iron beds were marshalled for cleaning and painting. The front room was converted into a bed-sitting room and the smaller chamber into a bathroom. The condition of Merrick's skin rendered a bath at least once a day a necessity, and I might here mention that with the use of the bath the unpleasant odour to which I have referred ceased to be noticeable. Merrick took up his abode in the hospital in December, 1886.
>
> Merrick now had something he had never dreamed of, never supposed to be possible – a home of his own for life. I at once began to make myself acquainted with him and to endeavour to understand his mentality. It was a study of much interest. I very soon learnt his speech so that I could talk freely with him. This afforded him great satisfaction, for, curiously enough, he had no one to talk to. I – having then much leisure – saw him almost every day, and made a point of spending some two hours with him every Sunday morning when he would chatter almost without ceasing. It was unreasonable to expect one nurse to attend to him continuously, but there was no lack of temporary volunteers. As they did not all acquire his speech it came about that I had occasionally to act as an interpreter.
>
> (Treves 1923)

Treves, for reasons which I suggest later, took an extraordinary interest in this incurable resident of the London. His clinical interest was becoming a human one:

> I found Merrick, as I have said, remarkably intelligent. He had

learnt to read and had become a most voracious reader. I think
he had been taught when he was in hospital with his diseased
hip. His range of books was limited. The Bible and Prayer Book
he knew intimately, but he had subsisted for the most part upon
newspapers, or rather upon such fragments of old journals as he
had chanced to pick up. He had read a few stories and some
elementary lesson books, but the delight of his life was a
romance, especially a love romance. These tales were very real to
him, as real as any narrative in the Bible, so that he would tell
them to me as incidents in the lives of people who had lived. In
his outlook upon the world he was a child, yet a child with some
of the tempestuous feelings of a man. He was an elemental being,
so primitive that he might have spent the twenty-three years of
his life immured in a cave.

(Treves 1923)

While Treves's kind intentions are above question, other of his
assumptions are not; nor is the motive for his kindness. Treves is
guilty of no very great offence here, except his native tendency to
romanticize. In describing Merrick's fascination with 'love romance'
he might as well be describing his own life-long addiction to the
romance of pirates, heroes and, it has to be said, love: all of these
figure strongly in his travel books. But Treves's urge to romanticize
also caused him to fictionalize, and to get things badly wrong. In *The
Elephant Man* he condemns Merrick's mother as a heartless woman of
no courage who abandoned her child. In reality, she was a frail,
religious woman who died from broncho-pneumonia when Merrick
was eleven. When his father remarried soon after his mother's death,
Merrick went to live with an uncle and tried to work at various jobs.
But his condition made employment impossible. It was only at this
point that Joseph ended up in the Leicester workhouse. This is
Treves's fanciful account of Merrick's early years:

Of his early days I could learn but little. He was very loath to
talk about the past. It was a nightmare, the shudder of which
was still upon him. He was born, he believed, in or about
Leicester. Of his father he knew absolutely nothing. Of his
mother he had some memory. It was very faint and had, I think,
been elaborated in his mind into something definite. Mothers
figured in the tales he had read, and he wanted his mother to be
one of those comfortable lullaby-singing persons who are so

44

loveable. In his subconscious mind there was apparently a germ of recollection in which someone figured who had been kind to him. He clung to this conception and made it more real by invention, for since the day when he could toddle no one had been kind to him. As an infant he must have been repellent, although his deformities did not become gross until he had attained his full stature.

It was a favourite belief of his that his mother was beautiful. The fiction was, I am aware, one of his own making, but it was a great joy to him. His mother, lovely as she may have been, basely deserted him when he was very small, so small that his earliest memories were of the workhouse to which he was taken. Worthless and inhuman as this mother was, he spoke of her with pride and even with reverence. Once, when referring to his own appearance, he said: 'It *is* very strange, for, you see, mother was so beautiful.'

The rest of Merrick's life up to the time that I met him at Liverpool Street Station was one dull record of degradation and squalor. He was dragged from town to town and from fair to fair as if he were a strange beast in a cage. A dozen times a day he would have to expose his nakedness and his piteous deformities before a gaping crowd who greeted him with such mutterings as 'Oh! What a horror! What a beast!'. He had had no childhood. He had had no boyhood. He had never experienced pleasure. He knew nothing of the joy of living nor of the fun of things. His sole idea of happiness was to creep into the dark and hide. Shut up alone in a booth, awaiting the next exhibition, how mocking must have sounded the laughter and merriment of the boys and girls outside who were enjoying the 'fun of the fair!' He had no past to look back upon and no future to look forward to. At the age of twenty he was a creature without hope. There was nothing in front of him but a vista of caravans creeping along a road, of rows of glaring show tents and of circles of staring eyes with, at the end, the spectacle of a broken man in a poor law infirmary.

Those who are interested in the evolution of character might speculate as to the effect of this brutish life upon a sensitive and intelligent man. It would be reasonable to surmise that he would become a spiteful and malignant misanthrope, swollen with venom and filled with hatred of his fellow-men, or, on the other hand, that he would degenerate into a despairing melancholic on the verge of idiocy. Merrick, however, was no such being. He had passed through the fire and had come out unscathed. His troubles had ennobled him. He showed himself to be a gentle, affectionate and loveable creature, as amiable as a happy woman, free from any trace of cynicism or resentment, without a grievance and without an unkind word for anyone. I have never heard him complain. I have never heard him deplore his ruined life or resent the treatment he had received at the hands of callous keepers. His journey through life had been indeed along a *via dolorosa*, the road had been uphill all the way, and now, when the night was at its blackest and the way most steep, he had suddenly found himself, as it were, in a friendly inn, bright with light and warm with welcome. His gratitude to those about him was pathetic in its sincerity and eloquent in the childlike simplicity with which it was expressed.

As I learnt more of this primitive creature I found that there were two anxieties which were prominent in his mind and which he revealed to me with diffidence. He was in the occupation of the rooms assigned to him and had been assured that he would be cared for to the end of his days. This, however, he found hard to realize, for he often asked me timidly to what place he would next be moved. To understand his attitude it is necessary to remember that he had been moving on and moving on all his life. He knew no other state of existence. To him it was normal. He had passed from the workhouse to the hospital, from the hospital back to the workhouse, then from this town to that town or from one showman's caravan to another. He had never known a home nor any semblance of one. He had no possessions. His sole belongings, besides his clothes and some books, were the monstrous cap and the cloak. He was a wanderer, a pariah and an outcast. That his quarters at the hospital were his for life he could not understand. He could not rid his mind of the anxiety which had pursued him for so many years – where am I to be taken next?

Another trouble was his dread of fellow men, his fear of people's eyes, the dread of being always stared at, the lash of the cruel mutterings of the crowd. In his home in Bedstead Square he was secluded; but now and then a thoughtless porter or a wardmaid would open his door to let curious friends have a peep at the Elephant Man. It therefore seemed to him as if the gaze of the world followed him still.

Influenced by these two obsessions he became, during his first few weeks at the hospital, curiously uneasy. 'When I am next moved can I go to a blind asylum or to a lighthouse?' He had read about blind asylums in the newspapers, and was attracted by the thought of being among people who could not see. The lighthouse has another charm. It meant seclusion from the curious. There at least no one could open a door and peep in at him. There he would forget that he had once been the Elephant Man. There he would escape the vampire showman. He had never seen a lighthouse, but he had come upon a picture of the Eddystone, and it appeared to him that this lonely column of stone in the waste of the sea was such a home as he longed for.

(Treves 1923)

In one sense Treves understood very well the degradation that Merrick had faced since childhood. It was not so much that he had every minute of the day to be an object of disgust because of his appearance; he had suffered, over a very long period, the prostitution of his deformity through forced exposure of his nakedness to anyone who would pay to look. Merrick was the ultimate outsider. The potency of myth surrounding him in film and on the stage is in part due to the fact that he bundles together all of the themes of alienation and exploitation of the period in one unfortunate character. Treves would not allow Merrick a mirror because both found the consequence of looking too unsettling. Treves felt a certain guilt over Merrick because he somehow seemed to throw back at him the possibility of ugliness in his own carefully ordered world in particular, and the carefully ordered world of England at the height of empire in general. His solution to Merrick's discomfort – which was at once sensitive and crude – was to introduce him forcibly to female beauty:

I wanted him to get accustomed to his fellow-men, to become a human being himself and to be admitted to the communion of his kind. He appeared day by day less frightened, less haunted looking, less anxious to hide, less alarmed when he saw his door being opened. He got to know most of the people about the place, to be accustomed to their comings and goings, and to realize that they took no more than a friendly notice of him. He could only go out after dark, and on fine nights ventured to take

47

a walk in Bedstead Square clad in his black cloak and his cap. His greatest adventure was on one moonless evening when he walked alone as far as the hospital garden and back again.

To secure Merrick's recovery and to bring him, as it were, to life once more, it was necessary that he should make the acquaintance of men and women who would treat him as a normal and intelligent young man and not as a monster of deformity. Women I felt to be more important than men in bringing about this transformation. Women were then more frightened of him, the more disgusted at his appearance and the more apt to give way to irresponsible expressions of aversion when they came into his presence. Moreover, Merrick had an admiration of women of such a kind that it attained almost to adoration. This was not the outcome of his personal experience. They were not real women but the products of his imagination. Among them was the beautiful mother surrounded, at a respectful distance, by heroines from the many romances he had read.

His first entry to the hospital was attended by a regrettable incident. He had been placed on the bed in the little attic, and a nurse had been instructed to bring him some food. Unfortunately she had not been fully informed of Merrick's unusual appearance. As she entered the room she saw on the bed, propped up by white pillows, a monstrous figure as hideous as an Indian idol. She at once dropped the tray she was carrying and fled, with a shriek, through the door. Merrick was too weak to notice much, but the experience, I am afraid, was not new to him.

He was looked after by volunteer nurses whose ministrations were somewhat formal and constrained. Merrick, no doubt, was conscious that their service was purely official, that they were merely doing what they were told to do and that they were acting rather as automata than as women. They did not help him feel that he was of their kind. On the contrary they, without knowing it, made him aware that the gulf of separation was almost immeasurable.

Feeling this, I asked a friend of mine, a young and pretty widow, if she thought she could enter Merrick's room with a smile, wish him good morning and shake him by the hand. She said she could and she did. The effect upon poor Merrick was not quite what I had expected. As he let go her hand he bent his head on his knees and sobbed until I thought he would never cease. The interview was over. He told me afterwards that this was the first woman who had ever smiled at him, and the first woman, in the whole of his life, who had shaken hands with him. From this day the transformation of Merrick commenced and he began to change, little by little, from a hunted thing into a man. It was a wonderful change to witness and one that never ceased to fascinate me.

(Treves 1923)

One can't help being reminded of the history of the London Hospital as a charity institution, in which the cured were obliged to give thanks to financial benefactors, doctors and God for a continued lease of life. Treves's motives were genuine; but Merrick's situation was that of the grateful beneficiary. After the pretty widow's visit, Merrick became the object of a more genteel freak show which brought him a steady flow of society ladies, culminating in a visit by the Princess of Wales. Was this genuine compassion, or merely fashion?

Merrick's case attracted much mention in the papers, with the result that he had a constant succession of visitors. Everybody wanted to see him. He must have been visited by almost every lady of note in the social world. They were all good enough to welcome him with a smile and to shake hands with him. The Merrick whom I had found shivering behind a rag of curtain in an empty shop was now conversant with duchesses and countesses and other ladies of high degree. They brought him presents, made his room bright with ornaments and pictures, and, what pleased him more than all, supplied him with books. He soon had a large library and most of his day was spent in reading. He was not the least spoiled; not the least puffed up; he never asked for anything; never presumed upon the kindness meted out to him, and was always humbly and profoundly grateful. Above all he lost his shyness. He liked to see his door pushed open and people to look in. He became acquainted with most of the frequenters of Bedstead Square, would chat with them at his window and show them some of his choicest presents. He improved in his speech, although in the end his utterances were not easy for strangers to understand. He was beginning, moreover, to be less conscious of his unsightliness, a little disposed to think it was, after all, not so very extreme. Possibly this was aided by the circumstances that I would not allow a mirror of any kind in his room.

The height of his social development was reached on an eventful day when Queen Alexandra – then Princess of Wales – came to the hospital to pay him a special visit. With that kindness which has marked every act of her life, the Queen entered Merrick's room smiling and shook him warmly by the hand. Merrick was transported with delight. This was beyond even his most extravagant dream. The Queen has made many people happy, but I think no gracious act of hers has ever caused such happiness as she brought into Merrick's room when she sat by his chair and talked to him as to a person she was glad to see.

Merrick, I may say, was now one of the most contented creatures I have chanced to meet.

(Treves 1923)

In April 1890 Merrick died in his sleep:

He was lying on his back as if asleep, and had evidently died suddenly without a struggle, since not even the coverlet of the bed was disturbed. The method of his death was peculiar. So large and so heavy was his head that he could not sleep lying down. When he assumed the recumbent position the passive skull was inclined to drop backwards, with the result that he experienced no little distress. The attitude he was compelled to assume when he slept was very strange. He sat up in bed with his back supported by pillows, his knees were drawn up, and his arms clasped round his legs, while his head rested on the points of his bent knees.

He often said to me that he wished he could lie down to sleep 'like other people'. I think on this last night he must, with some determination, have made the experiment. The pillow was soft, and the head, when placed on it, must have fallen backwards and caused a dislocation of the neck. Thus it came about that his death was due to the desire that had dominated his life – the pathetic but hopeless desire to be 'like other people'.

(Treves 1923)

Why did Treves take such an interest in Merrick? One answer is that under his own gruff exterior was a deeply rooted sentimentality which had two sources. The first was that sentimentality was a feature of the age, and Treves was nothing if not of his age. The second lies in the fact that surgery is a profession which can affect operators in two ways. One is that they distance themselves from the pain and death they cannot prevent, or even bring about by their own mistakes; the other is that they cultivate a certain brand of stoical sympathy towards patients in particular and the human race in general.

Merrick presented Treves with an opportunity to 'atone' for the pain and suffering he presided over in the operating theatre and on the surgical wards. Often he could not cure; all he could do was comfort. In one sense Merrick the incurable stood in Treves's imagination for all the pain and suffering of humanity. By arranging for his comfort, Treves expiated his own 'sins' of failure and omission.

But there were other factors at work. Treves's actions can be understood as an act of charity springing not only from Christianity, but from a bourgeois sense of social responsibility: the fortunate should help the less fortunate. They are also rooted in the intense desire of the late Victorians to *normalize* the world, to order it, to erase difference, to impose moral rule: the project of empire. Merrick, by the very fact of his existence, challenged that desired order. He represented a challenge to beauty, the perfectability of man, progress, and – through the prejudiced eyes of freak show attenders – goodness. To discover noble sentiment in such a creature, to discover humanity in that pitiable form, placed a special burden on Treves. Merrick would have to become *like other people*. But Treves's programme was so exaggerated that the unfortunate Merrick became even more *unlike* other people, ultimately presiding over a salon which entertained the Princess of Wales, Madge Kendall and other ladies of note.

There is also lurking in Merrick's story an aspect of the noble savage theme. In his idealization of Merrick, Treves places him even further outside the boundaries of 'normal' humanity. And in romanticizing him, Treves also does great violence, as in his erroneous fantasy of Merrick's mother.

That being said, one cannot ignore the genuine kindness which Treves showed. But for his calling card, Merrick probably would have died destitute in the most appalling circumstances.

Chapter Five

APPENDICITIS

'My father knew all the distinguished Victorian surgeons and physicians, especially Sir Frederick Treves,' said [Paul] Fildes, 'so when, as a boy, I got an attack of appendicitis, Victor Horsley did the operation because Treves was away in South Africa at the time. Later, in 1901, the pain returned, for Horsley had only partially removed my appendix at the first operation, leaving the stump. I remember Treves standing at one side of my bed and Sir Thomas Barlow at the other. Treves said peevishly:

"I do wish Horsley would stick to his bloody skulls and leave bellies to me."

Old Tommy Barlow was a bit shocked at Treves's language.

"I hope, my boy," he said to me, "that you will keep to yourself any expressions of this kind made by Sir Frederick Treves."'

Sir Luke Fildes's son Paul in conversation with J. Johnston Abraham.

(Abraham 1958)

Appendicitis is one of the most common serious complaints that surgeons treat. Nowadays it is little cause for alarm to be admitted to hospital, to be operated on that day or the next, and to spend forty-eight hours in hospital before returning home for a week's rest. If untreated, however, the appendix bursts and the material introduced into the abdomen induces peritonitis. The result can be fatal.

For decades surgeons understood what peritonitis was and routinely made the diagnosis. But the prognosis was usually gloomy. The reason was that large numbers of cases of peritonitis were due to appendicitis, but it was only in the late 1880s, when the study of anatomy led surgery into its golden age, that the true source of much peritonitis was identified as coming from the appendix. Just as scrofula had proved to be a chimera, so the frequency of peritonitis led to a diagnosis of perityphlitis which existed for years as a general diagnosis which avoided the true cause.

As in the search for the structure of DNA, as in the development of penicillin, appendicitis provided an opportunity for a 'race', for a scientific contest in which the goal was to be first. Treves believed – and many of his colleagues shared this view – that he had finished in the money in the great appendicitis race.

In 1892 Treves read an article in the American weekly *Medical News* which stated that Thomas G. Morton of Philadelphia was the first man to 'deliberately seek for and remove' the appendix. Treves wrote an ironical letter to the editor:

I have just read with interest a leading article in *The Medical News* for August 6th on the matter of operative treatment in inflammation of the vermiform appendix.

The fact that I live in a remote island, and, further, that a holiday of two months has taken me away from the haunts of books, must explain this tardy allusion to that paper.

The article discusses the origin of the operation for removing the vermiform appendix, and it is stated that to Dr Thomas G Morton belongs the credit of devising this procedure; the suggestion is made that the operation should be called 'Morton's operation', and it is asserted that Morton's operation embodies one of the most important and radical advances of modern surgery. Dr Morton thus becomes the founder of what will, I suppose, be known as 'Appendiceal Surgery' – should the present love for ridiculous terms survive.

I gather that Dr Morton's first operation was performed in 1888, and was reported in the Philadelphia County Medical Society's *Transactions* for that year. The nature of the operation is not stated. Who first excised the appendix vermiformis some musty and forgotten tome will no doubt reveal in the course of time. I know that the cecum was wholly removed (with success, by the by) by Arnaud, in 1732, but I have not yet completed my inquiries into the past surgical history of its appendage. So far as modern times are concerned, I should say that we owe the little item of surgical treatment under discussion to the admirable writings of [Reginald] Fitz, whose chief monograph appeared in 1886. In 1886 a patient with relapsing typhlitis came under my care in the London Hospital, and after due consideration I proposed to 'deliberately seek for and remove' his appendix. I operated on him during a period of apparently perfect health, on February 16th, 1887, and was able to correct the distortion of the appendix without actually excising it. He made a perfect recovery. On September 19th, 1887, I brought the matter before the Royal Medical and Chirurgical Society. The paper was read in February, 1888. I advised the treatment of selected cases of relapsing typhlitis by the deliberate removal of the offending appendix during a quiescent period. The proposal was not well received. In due course, however, an exuberant reaction took place, and of late years appendices have been removed with a needless and illogical recklessness which has brought this little branch of surgery into well-merited disrepute.

Discussions on questions of priority constitute the most pitiable and petty items in the literature of medicine. Time disposes of all such questions with absolute justice. The object of this letter is merely to bring up from oblivion an unpretending paper which lies buried in the annals of an ancient society.

(Treves 1892)

In one sense Treves's motive in objecting to the pettiness of 'priority' was authentic. His spell in Wirksworth had taught him that small-mindedness, vanity and professional jealousy were among the greatest obstacles to medical progress. On the other hand, Treves had a substantial ego, and he preferred to be a winner. His preoccupation with invention also tells us that he liked to be first.

The great appendicitis race features many competing claims to priority, and the search for them is as interesting as the race itself. If one goes back through the literature to 1938 (by which time it might be assumed the matter had been settled) one finds the following letter from Mr Samuel Jones of Rhodesia, to the *Lancet*:

It may interest you to know that it is now just on fifty years since the first operation for the removal of the vermiform appendix was performed. It was performed in I think June 1888 by Mr (afterwards Sir) Frederick Treves upon myself at my father's house. I thought you might perhaps care to refer to it in your journal as the operation subsequently became so usual. (I wish Mr Treves and I had patented it.)

The editor of the *Lancet* commented:

Mr Smith may well be right for on Feb. 4th, 1888, Mr Treves had reported to the Royal Medico-Chirurgical society a case of relapsing typhlitis in a man aged 34 in which he had intended to remove the appendix and did not. The abdomen was opened during a symptomless period after the subsidence of a second attack, and a kinked appendix was found which became straight at once after division of its mesentery. Treves forbore to remove it; the patient made a perfect recovery and up to the time of the report had remained free from further relapses. To Morton of Philadelphia is given credit for the earliest of all appendicectomies (in 1887), and in this country Treves had many runners-up. At the same meeting of the Royal Medico-Chirurgical society Mr Timothy Holmes reported removal of part of the appendix of a man aged 30, and Mr Howard Marsh mentioned the case of a girl who died from peritonitis from whom he had too late removed the appendix. Mr Thomas Bryant, on the other hand, said he had never removed the vermiform appendix, although he felt there must be cases in which it was desirable.

Treves's claim to British priority in the matter of identifying and surgically treating appendicitis (which is not the same as removing the appendix) is asserted by Howell and Ford in *The True History of the Elephant Man* (1980), who claim he was responsible for 'the first operation undertaken in Britain to treat chronic, relapsing appendicitis'. In 1935, Sir D'Arcy Power wrote that 'the case reported by Mr Frederick Treves appears to have been the first in this country which was undertaken deliberately for the cure of a chronic and relapsing inflammation, though he did not remove the appendix'.

In 1938 W. J. Bishop offered a more scholarly survey of the question which drove its origins back to antiquity. 'Cases of appendicitis were almost certainly observed by Hippocrates, the Father of Medicine, and unmistakable evidence of the condition has been found in Egyptian mummies of the Byzantine period.' Bishop reminds us that

The first description of the appendix as an anatomical organ was given in 1524 by Berengorious Corpus, Professor of Surgery at

Pavia and Bologna; and it was figured by the great Andrea
Vesalius in his work on *The Fabric of the Human Body*, published in
1543. One of the most accurate of the early reports is that of the
German surgeon Laurence Heister, based upon the dissection of
the body of a malefactor executed at Altdorff in 1711.

(Bishop 1938)

In his search for a British precedent, Bishop concludes that in July
1883 'Sir Charters Symonds, at the suggestion of Dr F. A. Mahomed,
removed a concretion from the appendix of a patient in Guy's Hospital'. But his researches oblige him to conclude that

The first surgeon actually to remove the diseased appendix was
Thomas G. Morton of Philadelphia in 1887. Treves's first
appendicectomy was performed in 1888 [sic]. . . . In a series of
articles beginning in 1886, Reginald H. Fitz of Boston finally
related the origin of the disease to the appendix, laid down the
principles of diagnosis and treatment, and first used the term
'appendicitis'.

(Bishop 1938)

The question of who was responsible for what in the appendicitis
race did a great deal to encourage the history of medicine in Britain.
In 1947 George Bankoff built on Bishop's work to offer a view that

By the end of the nineteenth century there was very little left in
the abdomen that surgeons did not dare to assail. Diseased gall-
bladders were removed, and in America Charles McBurney of
Massachusetts was able to demonstrate that most of the
abdominal pains and peritonitis were due to inflammation of a
small portion of the intestine known as the appendix. It was also
an American – Fitz – who gave appendicitis its name in 1886.
There were other surgeons, particularly in England, who had
reported cases before McBurney. Hancock opened an abscess for
perforated appendix in Charing Cross Hospital forty years before
McBurney, but his patient died. Kronlein, a German, also
records an operation for perforated appendix, but he thought
that the appendix was only a casual finding. According to him it
was the first portion of the large intestine that was responsible;
the little appendix was neglected as being superfluous. It was,
therefore, McBurney who clarified the diagnosis and showed
beyond doubt that the appendix was to be blamed for the

majority of abdominal infections. In 1883 he performed successfully an appendectomy, showing also the best point at which to open the abdomen – a line midway from the umbilicus and the pelvic bone. This spot is known as McBurney's point. In England the operation became famous when Edward VII nearly died from appendicitis and was operated on successfully by Sir Frederick Treves; from that date appendicitis became the fashionable disease.

(Bankoff 1947)

In his article on appendicitis in *The British Encyclopaedia of Medical Practice* (second edition, 1950) V. Zachary Cope supports Fitz's claim to fame by stating that he 'was not the first to observe an inflamed appendix, but he was the first to describe its definite signs and to bring these to the notice of the profession'. But Cope adds a new competitor by revealing that an American surgeon, Willard Parker, established the value of opening perityphlitic abscesses (as opposed to removing the appendix) in 1867, while agreeing that 'the first surgeon deliberately to operate for and remove an inflamed appendix with a successful result was T. G. Morton of Philadelphia, in 1886'. As an afterthought he adds, 'in England Sir Frederick Treves advocated operation for appendicitis, but for almost twenty years the European countries were slow to adopt early operative treatment'.

One would have thought that by 1950, when Cope's article appeared, the great appendicitis race would have been settled. Not so. Two articles by John Shepherd in the *Lancet* in 1954 and 1956 take the race back to the eighteenth century. In an historical overview (1954), Shepherd notes that while the Egyptians recognized the appendix as an anatomical structure, 'clear observations of the pathological changes in the appendix seldom occur before 1800'. He attributes the first English appendectomy to Claudius Amyand, a surgeon at St George's Hospital, a fellow of the Royal Society and sergeant-surgeon to King George II who, in 1736, published a paper in *Philosophical Transactions* with the grand title 'Of an inguinal rupture with a pin in the Appendix Caeci, incrusted with stone, and some observations on Wounds in the Guts'. The case involved

a boy of 11 named Hanvil Anderson, and the hernia had been present from infancy. Amyand decided that an associated faecal fistula could be cured only by cure of the hernia. He explored the scrotal swelling and found the appendix perforated by an

57

encrusted pin. With some difficulty he separated omentum and appendix. The latter was doubled on itself. It was amputated and a stump one inch long was left because a fistula was anticipated. The hernial sac was removed and the fistulous tract excised. Healing was rapid and the stump ligature separated on the tenth day without incident. The operation took 'near half an hour' – a tribute to the skill of the surgeon and the fortitude of the small boy.

(Shepherd 1954)

In Shepherd's opinion, 'Claudius Amyand deserves the title of the pioneer of surgery of the vermiform appendix'.

Shepherd further complicates previous accounts by noting, without reference to historians who seemed to have missed these points, that it had previously been 'customary' to attribute the first appendix operation to the French physician Mestivier, who published an account in 1759. Returning to the original French text, Shepherd's own translation reveals that Mestivier's account is merely a description of a foreign body in the appendix. Shepherd shows that the English surgeon James Parkinson came close to making Fitz's discovery in 1812 when, performing an autopsy on a boy of five who had died after an illness of only two days, he recorded a perforation of the appendix. But Parkinson offered no commentary on the fact.

In 1824 the Frenchman Louyer-Villermay described two fatal cases of perforation and 'emphasized that the appendix in each case was the primary source of trouble and that the caecum was in no way involved'. This is the essence of Fitz's discovery, succinctly stated sixty years before Fitz published. In fact, the French were then far ahead of anyone else in this area. But knowledge which would have advanced surgery by more than half a century and saved many thousands of lives was lost in a squabble between doctors. Shepherd explains:

About this time the French surgeon Dupuytren exerted a powerful influence, and he insisted that 'tumeurs phlegnoseuses' of the right side of the abdomen had their origin in disease of the caecum. The German surgeons Goldbeck and Puchelt supported this view and defined a disease perityphlitis which on occasion resulted in the collection of pus around the caecum. The conception of perityphlitis was based on inaccurate anatomical observation and incomplete pathological deductions. The acceptance of this entirely theoretical disease retarded the understanding of appendicitis for more than fifty years.

In 1827 Melier in France reprinted the two case reports given by Louyer-Villermay and added six additional examples of acute appendicitis. This is the first paper in which there is any detailed discussion of appendicitis. Melier noted the change in symptoms in a patient whose appendix had perforated and he described the sequence of symptoms by which the disease might be diagnosed. ... He was, therefore, the first to envisage the possible benefit of early appendectomy in acute disease.

(Shepherd 1954)

Typhlitis and perityphlitis were mere word play, terms invented to hide the fact that doctors did not understand the nature of the problem. Curiously, they were terms to which Treves clung tenaciously (even after they had been discredited) despite his dislike of unclear thinking and language. Perhaps one reason for their acceptance in Britain was that British doctors, if they understood a foreign language at all, were likely to be able to read German, and the concepts were invented by Germans. It is possible that the early French advances in the appendicitis race were ignored in Britain because most doctors did not understand French, and might not have been inclined to want to. There was also a strong element of xenophobia in Treves's determination not to employ the term appendicitis because the word was, in his view, a clumsy American neologism.

The terms perityphlitis and typhlitis were really concerned with symptoms rather than causes. The former referred to inflammation *around* the caecum (the part of the large intestine in the lower right hand corner of the abdomen from which the appendix protrudes), while the latter referred to inflammation *of* the caecum. But even if one discounts the French advances in this area, many English surgeons in the early nineteenth century were identifying the appendix as the seat of disease, yet, for some reason, were ignored. An article in the *Lancet* by Thompson and Baller in 1834 identifies the appendix as culprit in its very title: 'Two cases of fatal enteritis caused by hardened faeculent material in the appendix caeci'. In 1837 and 1839 John Burne published articles stressing the importance of the appendix. In 1837 Burne 'is quite definite in saying that acute inflammation in the right iliac fossa is most often caused by appendicular disease'. His

1839 paper 'contains a full account of acute perforative appendicitis'. Even Bright and Addison's popular textbook of 1839, *The Practice of Medicine*, 'described with accuracy the clinical signs and the usual course of appendicitis', and expressed the view that 'appendicular disease was much more common than primary inflammation of the caecum'. Yet this information had no impact on current thinking, despite the book being a standard text. In 1848, Europe's year of revolution, an English surgeon called Hancock successfully drained an appendicular abscess – precisely the same operation Treves would perform on King Edward in 1902. Eleven years later, in 1859, the Frenchman Leudet 'stated categorically that perforation of the appendix was more common than all other types of gastro-intestinal perforation put together'. What could be clearer? Leudet must also be credited with the first suggestion that laxatives should not be given during an attack of acute appendicitis.

What Shepherd's survey of the eighteenth century and the first half of the nineteenth century shows is that acute appendicitis had been very clearly established both clinically and pathologically. Yet two words – perityphlitis and typhlitis – ensured that the obvious and proven would remain unnoticed.

During the second half of the nineteenth century abdominal surgery became more common because of the three A's – antisepsis, anaesthetics and anatomy – and the appendix figured largely in this area. But still there was no breakthrough. In 1867 the American Willard Parker described three stages of acute appendicitis (gangrene, perforating ulcer and abscess) and published details of four operations in which he drained abscesses. Parker also advocated surgery during a quiescent period, usually between the fifth and twelfth days of the attack. It is an interesting gloss on Parker's career to note that questions of priority can depend on many things – for instance, the existence of a technique whereby knowledge can be acted upon. 'Hancock had made the same point [regarding operating during the interval], but Parker is given the credit because his opinion was promulgated at a time when abdominal surgery – through Lister's work and with the advances in anaesthesia – had become a realistic possibility' (Shepherd 1954).

British surgeons were on the whole conservative at this time, and the interval operation was destined to become standard procedure (in Britain). In Germany, however, Mikulicz urged in 1884 that the inflamed appendix should be removed during the acute stage – which is, of course, what is done today. Shepherd claims that Kronlein was the first to put Mikulicz's theory into practice:

> In February, 1884, he diagnosed an acute abdomen as being due to either a perforated appendix or acute ileal obstruction. Through a midline incision he removed the appendix and did the accustomed thorough antiseptic lavage of the peritoneal cavity. The patient died two days later. In July, 1885, Kronlein operated on another such case. There was a general peritonitis and after an hour and a half he had failed to locate the appendix. The peritoneal cavity was closed without drainage after the usual cleansing and irrigation. Ironically enough, this patient recovered! Kronlein published these reports in 1886 and acknowledges his debt to Mikulicz and to Lawson Tait (1883) who had shortly before published his account of 208 abdominal sections and so stimulated an interest in abdominal surgery. Kronlein must, therefore, be credited with the first planned attempt to cure a patient of acute appendicitis by urgent laparotomy and by a removal of the appendix.
>
> (Shepherd 1954)

And the diagnosis and treatment could not have been spelled out more clearly in England when in 1883 C. J. Symonds wrote,

> the difficulty very often of diagnosing the cause of sudden abdominal pain and the number of cases of typhlitis that recover will long deter us from opening the abdomen and removing the appendix and yet post-mortem inspection shows that if such a procedure could be undertaken a recovery might have been possible in some otherwise hopeless cases.

Shepherd's account is not only embarrassing to other historians because of its revelations of overlooked eighteenth- and early nineteenth-century contenders in the great appendicitis race; it also shows that Morton, universally reckoned to be the winner on the surgical side, was in fact a runner-up. Morton's operation was in April 1887, when he diagnosed appendicitis and successfully removed most of the offending organ. The patient recovered. However, in May 1886 Hall of New York was operating on a seventeen-year-old boy for an inguinal hernia. During the operation he discovered a perforated appendix and removed it. So, although appendicitis had not been diagnosed *before* the abdomen was opened, Shepherd noted in 1954 that the most accurate historical knowledge showed that Hall's was probably the third appendectomy ever, and the first in the US. Hall was unaware of his predecessors Amyand and Kronlein.

Fitz was breathing down Hall's neck, and his 1886 paper, 'Perforating inflammation of the vermiform appendix', delivered at the first ever meeting of the American Association of Physicians, was the epoch-making event which eventually put paid to typhlitis and perityphlitis and established appendicitis as a universally acknowledged clinical entity. He is responsible for the view that urgent diagnosis and treatment were essential.

What the history of appendicitis to this point shows is that medicine, despite its presentation of itself as a science, was subject to curious whims, prejudices, fancies and beliefs which hindered progress. And it could be a victim of language. The creation of the word 'appendicitis' was the precondition for the long history of the disease to be admitted to the canon of surgical knowledge. Like scrofula, perityphlitis and typhlitis had to be relegated to the status of beliefs.

Many writers still credit Treves with the first appendix operation in Britain (February 1887). But Shepherd was able to add an extraordinary postscript to his historical researches after studying the career of the British surgeon Lawson Tait.

I indicated [in 1954] that the German surgeon Mikulicz was the first to suggest that acute appendicitis might be diagnosed preoperatively, and that the correct treatment was the early removal of the appendix. It has long been accepted that Kronlein (1886) was the first to remove successfully an acutely inflamed appendix after considering this diagnosis preoperatively. Kronlein did this operation in July 1885 and acknowledges a debt to Mikulicz and to Lawson Tait as the instigators of his approach to the problem of management of acute appendicitis.

In my paper I suggested that Lawson Tait was probably the first to diagnose and remove an acutely inflamed appendix in Britain, and drew attention to his description in the *British Medical Journal* (Tait 1899) of a drainage operation for appendicitis. In this article he wrote, 'I have twice in cases very similar removed the vermiform appendix ... both my cases recovered. I am disposed to think that the risk of operation is somewhat increased by this detail'. Until recently the reports of

these earlier appendicectomies by Lawson Tait have eluded me.
It is now clear, from an article entitled 'Surgical treatment of
typhlitis' in the *Birmingham Medical Review* (Tait 1890), not only
that Lawson Tait was the first British surgeon to diagnose acute
appendicitis and treat the condition by removal of the appendix,
but also that he did the first of these operations in May, 1880 –
his successful operation preceeding Kronlein's by five years. The
second patient was operated on in 1886.

(Shepherd 1956)

So, the league table is revised. After Amyand, Tait becomes the
author of the second ever appendectomy, beating the Americans Hall
and Morton. But the truly astonishing fact unearthed by Shepherd
(1956) is that despite his successes with the two appendix operations,
Tait then reverted to a conservative policy of only draining the
abscess, leaving the appendix intact. The great appendicitis race
becomes both farce and tragedy in view of the fact that, 'Had Tait not
abhorred the expression "appendicitis" he would long ago have been
credited with the initial advances in the management of the disease'.
And although he 'recanted after his early successes he should be
recognised as the pioneer in the treatment of acute appendicitis'.

*   *   *

Quite apart from the international scrabble for priority in the great
appendicitis race was a more local dispute which involved Treves and
a quirky Liverpool doctor by the name of Hugh Owen Thomas. The
dispute was over priority in the medical rather than surgical treatment of acute abdomens in general. Treves's first major work on this
subject was *Intestinal Obstruction* (1884), which won the Royal College
of Surgeon's Jacksonian Prize in 1883. It was a spectacularly successful book which was reprinted in 1888 and 1890, with revised editions
in 1899 and 1902. It was immediately hailed by the *British Medical
Journal*'s reviewer as 'a very complete monograph on intestinal obstruction, a standard work on a subject that has not been so compre-
hensively treated by any contemporary English writer'.

Treves and Thomas locked horns after a famous debate on intestinal obstruction in Liverpool in 1885. As a surgeon, Treves's
ultimate cure for obstruction was surgery. Some physicians who
eschewed surgical intervention advocated simple medical treatment
of bed rest and opium. Thomas was slightly peculiar in that, as a

surgeon, he advanced the physician's case. He took the view that surgery was inappropriate and that bed rest was the right 'cure' for obstruction. When one of the speakers at the 1885 conference told Thomas that his bed rest and opium regime was 'an established medical treatment', Thomas was outraged. He somehow believed that he had invented the regime, and that any mention of it should include reference to himself. While the history of medicine contains many displays of ego, temper and pettiness, Thomas's case is exceptional. He was one of those peculiar individuals who have always to be right, but to be right alone: by agreeing with him, one was guilty of plagiarism.

After the 1885 conference Thomas attempted to publish papers on obstruction in a Liverpool medical journal, but was rebuffed by the editor who advised that 'he would do better to write on a subject that he understood'. The aftermath of the conference produced a lengthy correspondence in the medical press. In one letter, Thomas complained that the bed rest and opium option which Treves referred to in his book on intestinal obstruction had not been credited to him. Treves replied with careful courtesy in the *Lancet*:

> With regard to the claim made on behalf of Mr Thomas, I regret that I did not see his able and original monograph until the MS of my book was entirely in type. The chief feature of Mr Thomas's work appeared to me to consist in a very skilful and vigorous advocacy of the measure now in question – a measure the value of which I considered had been for years generally recognised. I cannot agree with Mr Thomas in considering this particular treatment as final and all sufficient. It appears to me to be the best primary routine treatment, and the best introduction to such other and more active measures as the needs of particular cases may possibly demand.

This absurd episode concluded with Thomas's publication of a tract pompously titled *The Collegian of 1666 and the Collegians of 1885; or What is Recognised Treatment?* (second edition, 1888) which is a bitter attack on Treves and others. The collegian of 1666 was the great English physician Thomas Sydenham, who is characterized as having defended the role of physician against the upstart surgeons. 'In the course of the argument . . . the place of the surgeon is clearly defined as being no more than that of the physician's assistant.' This is a very curious position for a surgeon to take, and perhaps Thomas should be seen as the first anti-surgeon. His position was exceedingly reactionary, and his treatment of obstruction little more advanced than Sydenham's own advice that the best way to apply heat to the affected parts was to place a kitten on the patient's belly. In his conclusion, Thomas simply rejects the truth of mortality figures when he protests that 'Mr Treves's classification, like the recognised treatment, is too mechanical. The severest forms of obstruction almost take care of themselves.'

By comparison with Thomas, Treves was a great innovator in the treatment of obstruction. In the 1899 edition of *Intestinal Obstruction* he boldly proclaimed, 'it is less dangerous to leap from the Clifton Suspension Bridge than to suffer from acute intestinal obstruction and decline operation'. But hindsight reveals an essential conservatism in Treves's approach to the problem. In their definitive account of the rise of surgery Owen and Sarah Wangensteen note that

> Treves could not ignore completely the orthodox practice of the day. In publishing his revised monograph, therfore, he still included such conventional procrastinating treatments as posture, opium, purgation, metallic mercury, electricity, enemas, and inflation of the bowel with water, air and other gases. He listed, without endorsement, puncture of the bowel with a fine needle or trochar, and he mentioned, too, the more dangerous procedure of enterocentesis, in which the trochar or needle is left in the bowel for varying periods of time for temporary decompression or with the hope of establishing an external fistula.
>
> (Wangensteen and Wangensteen 1978)

While Treves's *Intestinal Obstruction* was continually updated, it is ultimately judged as conservative by the Wangensteens. 'After the Liverpool debates of 1885, the congresses of 1887 and 1889,' they write, 'one would reasonably have anticipated signs of improvement in the management of intestinal obstruction'; yet,

> As late as 1902, just a few days before Treves operated upon Edward VII, who was awaiting coronation, Treves stated that there is no disease in the appendix until the peritoneum is involved and advised that operation be delayed five days after the onset of the attack, except in 'ultra-acute' cases.
>
> (Wangensteen and Wangensteen 1978)

This conservatism was partly caused by Treves's demand for rigour and precision in a surgery founded on true anatomical principles. His Hunterian Lectures to the Royal College of Surgeons in 1885, *The Anatomy of the Intestinal Canal and Peritoneum in Man*, were landmarks in helping to establish abdominal surgery. The study was based on dissection of one hundred fresh bodies, foetuses and fourteen apes and other mammals for comparative purposes. By drawing the clearest map to date of the abdominal region, Treves made it easier for doctors to obtain accurate diagnoses (it must be remembered that the X-ray had not yet come into use) and to recommend correct treatment. Among his discoveries was the fact that everyone's guts were different, and he disproved the long held view that a true ratio obtained between the length of the intestines and 'the entire intestinal canal and the age, height and weight of the subject'. He gave a detailed account of the elaborate structure of the peritoneal folds. He pointed out that the sigmoid flexure

does not, as a rule, occupy the left iliac fossa, but the pelvis; the attachment of its mesentery crosses the psoas muscle at a right angle, and then takes a slight curve upwards, so that it does not arise wholly from the iliac fossa, as generally described; and, lastly, the flexure itself forms an omega-shaped, not a sigmoid, loop.

(Treves 1885)

These are hardly small, niggling details. If a surgeon had a faulty map of the territory in which he was working, the patient's chances of recovery were much reduced.

The impact of the Hunterian Lectures can be measured by the fact that Treves is remembered today by three eponymous terms resulting from them. The first is 'Treves's operation' for the evacuation of a psoas abscess. The second is 'Treves's hernia', 'an internal hernia in a fossa between the ileum and the appendix'. The third and most important eponym is 'Treves's folds', of which there are two types: the first is the ileocaecal fold, known as 'Treves's bloodless fold' ('a sheet of peritoneum which passes from the antimesometria border of the terminal ileum to the base of the appendix and neighbouring portion of the caecum'); the second is the ileocolic fold, or 'superior ileocaecal fold of Treves' ('a sheet of peritoneum passing from the ventral surface of the mesentery of the terminal ileum, in front of the ileocolic junction, to the anterior surface of the ascending colon near the caecum').

Despite these advances in anatomy, Treves continued to have an uneasy relationship with the appendix. At the end of his Hunterian Lectures he incorrectly suggested that the appendix might have a physiological function (it is in fact a vestigial organ). And he was reluctant to accept the work of the American Fitz. Fitz's study (Fitz 1886) of nearly five hundred cases resulted in a clear instruction as to the symptoms of appendicitis; its diagnosis ('Its usual site is in the right iliac fossa, below a line extending from the anterior superior spine of the ileum to the navel, nearer the former, and two fingers breadth above Poupart's ligament ... A rectal examination not infrequently permits the recognition of the tumour which abdominal palpitation fails to disclose'); and treatment – no laxatives to be given, and immediate surgical intervention. As Fitz's colleague John Homans put it, 'I decided not to wait for the autopsy but to operate at once'.

Fitz's contribution is one of the great moments in the history of medicine. One review of the literature in 1856 showed that out of forty-seven cases of 'typhlitis', only one survived. American statistics for 1935 showed that appendicitis ranked as the fifteenth most important cause of death, accounting for 16,142 in that year. Among policyholders of the Metropolitan Life Insurance Company appendicitis was the ninth most frequent cause of death. The impact of the diagnosis and treatment of appendicitis can be measured by the fact that, in 1973, with a much increased population, there were only 1,066 deaths from appendicitis in the US.

After Fitz, Treves continued to use the terms typhlitis and perityphlitis, albeit sceptically. In his 1888 account of his first appendix operation (in 1887), Treves refers to 'so-called typhlitis'. He accepted that the appendix could be the cause of much *relapsing* typhlitis. This is the source of his view that surgery should happen in the interval between attacks. The problem with this approach is that many patients died of a first acute attack, and so could not be candidates for interval surgery. And once the abscess had burst, even if the patient were eventually cured by an interval operation, his condition would be far more serious than it need be. Surprisingly for a surgeon, Treves thought that *acute* cases should be treated by medical means, along the lines advocated by his adversary Hugh Owen Thomas: bed rest and opiates.

Ironically, Treves's fastidiousness about language (which was usually in pursuit of a clearer explanation of a particular condition) was the very thing that prevented him from getting the treatment of appendicitis right. The term appendicitis does not appear in his writing until 1889 – three years after Fitz coined it. In this instance he uses it in a disparaging way, to dismiss the classification of inflammations into four categories according to what part of the anatomy was inflamed: typhlitis (caecum), perityphlitis (peritoneum), paratyphlitis (connective tissue around the caecum) and appendicitis (appendix). He argues, 'this classification has long since been shown to be unsound'. The last one had manifestly not. In 1896 he published an article on surgery of the peritoneum in which he contradicted Fitz's work by stating a belief that occasionally 'peritonitis is started by mischief in the caecum itself, the appendix being sound'. Also in 1896 Treves published his massive *A System of Surgery* in which he reinforced his conservative surgical views, and wrote that in the medical treatment of 'perityphlitis the application of half-a-dozen leeches often acts with magical effect'. He also advised the administration of laxatives in cases where the attack was not too severe – ten years after Fitz warned of the potentially fatal consequences of this. In 1897 he still had enough belief in perityphlitis to publish a monograph by that title, noting in his introduction that 'the uncouth name "appendicitis" has been given to this disease'.

In 1902, just a few days before he operated on King Edward VII, Treves gave the Cavendish Lecture on appendicitis to the West London Medico-Chirurgical Society at Hammersmith Town Hall. In it he surveyed the whole question of appendicitis and outlined his own more or less final position. One might have expected it to be more in line with American practice: it was not. He began with the sarcastic observation that: 'One knows that the academical-minded have a great objection to this uncouth term "appendicitis"; it lacks precision, but it has found its place in the clumsy nomenclature of medicine, and has been accepted by the public with an extraordinary amount of generosity.' But he was forced to admit,

I should imagine there has scarcely been anything more
remarkable in the way of medicine at the close of the nineteenth
century than the sudden appearance of the disease now known
as appendicitis. .... The disease is not new, but newly discovered;

it has been hidden for centuries under a lot of vague clinical facts and medical verbiage.

(Treves 1902)

Yet there is a degree of defensiveness masquerading as iconoclasm in Treves's reference to the term as 'ridiculous'. Of 'the ridiculous classification of appendicitis' he said:

Every monograph on the subject begins with a ridiculous list of forms of appendicitis – the gastric form and so on – and if you discuss a case with a medical man he often says: 'Do you think this is catarrhal or suppurative, or what is it?' This same elaborate classification has a place in the history of all maladies. There was a time, for instance, when there were about 15 or 20 forms of pleurisy and these all came down to one thing. How many forms of synovitis were there 20 years ago? How many forms are there now? Inflammation of the appendix, catarrh of the appendix – what does it lead to? Ulceration, stricture, perforation, gangrene. There is nothing to be gained by this ridiculous classification.

(Treves 1902)

The Hammersmith lecture has an aura of sour grapes about it, of a man who has stubbornly adhered to a view which others have proved incorrect. Treves singles out as a target for his scorn the American surgeon McBurney, who is remembered eponymously for having discovered 'McBurney's point' – the small area between the navel and the prominent anterior superior spine of the right iliac bone. (The first thing a doctor will do today in a suspected case of appendicitis is to palpate this area.) Perhaps the fact that Treves's three eponyms were all hidden away in the abdomen, and McBurney's one was prominent on the exterior of the body and more famous than all of his put together, played some part in the doggedness with which Treves attempted to discredit it. Treves had often brought his formidable rhetorical powers to bear on what he saw as nonsense and humbug in medicine. But McBurney's point did not deserve this tirade:

With regard to clinical matters it would be a gross waste of time of this society if I were to deal in any way with the clinical phenomena of this common trouble. But in this connexion I want to deal with one solitary point – with the so-called McBurney's point. Tenderness at this magic spot has become a

69

sort of talisman; it is an inspired sign, it is some sort of religious stigma, it is the touchstone of the disease. The hand of the experienced man is put on the spot and there is tenderness and the patient has got appendicitis. I need not remind you where this spot is, but let me say what is said of it. It is said to be always present in every case of appendicitis, it is said to be not present in other troubles met with in the abdomen. It is said to indicate the seat of the disease, it is said by some to indicate the position of the diseased appendix. It is said by others who are more cautious – by McBurney to wit – that it actually indicates the precise space of the appendix. Well, now, that is the most modest account that could be given of the possibilities of McBurney's point. Beyond that there is a great deal more, but that is keeping soberly within the limit of fact. The construction that I would venture to put upon it is this. There is a certain tenderness in the right iliac fossa in appendicitis and McBurney's point corresponds roughly to the centre of the right iliac fossa and therefore it is reasonably the place where tenderness is exhibited. Next it is a symptom quite common in other maladies, most notably in colitis. In the next place I should say that it is a feature exceedingly common in perfectly healthy individuals in a quite normal state. Last of all, it does not indicate the situation of the disease and it does not indicate, which McBurney insists that it does, the situation of the base of the appendix. Any man operating and cutting through the situation at this point will know perfectly well that there may be tenderness there and the base of the appendix does not correspond to that spot.

(Treves 1902)

Treves was so convinced that McBurney was in error that he mounted an extraordinary programme of 'research' in an effort to discredit the American:

Feeling that it was a matter that needed investigation I asked Dr A.[rthur] Keith if he would carry on investigations on certain lines that I indicated and I am deeply indebted to him for the admirable manner in which these investigations were carried out. What struck me was this. So many persons are tender at certain points in the right iliac fossa and very often acutely tender. But there is no such point on the left side and there must be something, therefore, anatomically different there. What is it? The ureter or what? This is how the facts came out. Sections were made along the spino-umbilical line; that line measures in the normal male adult six inches and it crosses the rectus muscle at the anatomical point known as Munro's point and it roughly corresponds there to McBurney's point. Well, now, the ureter has nothing to do with Munro's point because it does not cross the line there. Exactly the same condition exists on the left side, so that nothing is to be learnt from that. The next thing is this. The structure that exactly comes beneath that point is the ileo-caecal valve. The tender thing that can be discovered in the body of a healthy person at that exact spot is the ileo-caecal valve. As you know, all orifices are peculiarly well supplied with nerve fibres and are peculiarly sensitive, such as the sphincter of the anus, the orifice of the pylorus, and other sphincter-like openings. That this is the cause of the tenderness in that particular spot admits of no disrepute. The base of the appendix, you will be surprised to hear, is one inch below McBurney's point, as discovered in 50 bodies preserved in formalin. Dr Keith was good enough to examine the bodies of 27 living medical students with this result:— in 11 the point of tenderness was exactly on the point; in nine it was a little above the point; and in four it was a little below the point. Those data pretty nearly correspond pro rata with the condition found in 50 hardened bodies by formalin. Moreover, in only three out of 27 students was there any particularly tender spot in the right iliac fossa; in none was there any tenderness discovered on the left side of the body. That, I think, should render definite the circumstances about McBurney's point and the part it plays in this trouble.

(Treves 1902)

In this matter of diagnosis, Treves was wrong. He was also wrong when, discussing indications for surgical treatment, he claimed:

The second fact I do not think can be pressed too strongly is this. The very great majority of all cases of appendicitis get well spontaneously.... The third fact, which I think should be emphasised as strongly as the last one, is this: operation during an acute attack of appendicitis is attended with great risk to life.

(Treves 1902)

It is deeply ironical that while Treves continued to advocate the interval operation sixteen years after Fitz had demonstrated the necessity of immediate surgery, he claimed that his approach was revolutionary, and criticized his colleagues for not following *his* lead:

> Another matter that I will trouble you with is with regard to operative treatment carried out during the quiescent period. It so happened that in a paper which I read before the Royal Medical and Chirurgical Society in 1887 I ventured to suggest that appendicitis when relapsing should be treated by removal of the appendix during the quiescent period. Looking back on the discussion which followed that paper it is curious to note how very feebly it was received and how the method advocated therein was scarcely accepted at all as a reasonable method of treatment. In that particular discussion one physician of considerable experience said that in the whole of his life he had never seen a case of typhlitis that could possibly have called for surgical interference of any sort. So that the reception of that paper was one which, I must confess, condemned me very much. Still, I do not think one has any reason to complain of the infrequency with which the operation is carried out at the present day. I have since that particular date removed the appendix during the quiescent period over 1000 times and out of that number I have lost two patients. I could without being very Jesuitical exclude one of those cases because it was not primarily a case of appendicitis but where there was a mass in the right iliac fossa and where as a result the appendix was concerned. But I will acknowledge two deaths.
>
> (Treves 1902)

Treves's complaint is valid to the extent that, if anything, the majority of his colleagues were even more conservative than he was in the matter of appendicitis.

The real reason for Treves's conservatism over appendicitis is probably more personal than professional. At the end of 1900, when his daughter Hetty was eighteen, she was stricken with abdominal pain. Treves, the English authority on appendicitis, who scoffed at McBurney's point, did not suspect appendicitis. But that is precisely what she had. As the disease took its course, Hetty became feverish and, belatedly, her father realized that she had developed an advanced stage of peritonitis.

When it was already too late, Treves decided to operate on his own daughter. His friend D. G. Halsted relates that 'At the eleventh hour he called in two of his surgical colleagues, but they refused to take any responsibility for the case, pointing out that if he could not save her, no one could. Her death was a terrible blow to him' (Halsted 1959).

The circumstances are almost unimaginable. As a surgeon Treves was more than usually sensitive about his failures. To bungle the diagnosis of a fatal disease in one's own daughter, and then to fail to save her through operative means, was the worst tragedy that could befall him.

No record of Treves's grief survives; except, perhaps, an essay in *The Elephant Man and Other Reminiscences* (1923) entitled 'The idol with hands of clay'. It is presented as a true story of a young medical man who is highly qualified as a surgeon and as a physician. He marries a beautiful young wife and sets up in practice in a small country town. His wife adores him and believes that his medical knowledge makes him one of the cleverest men on earth. Working in a cottage hospital, the young doctor is rarely called upon to perform serious operations. Then, one day, his wife is taken ill. The diagnosis is appendicitis. The doctor has never performed an appendectomy, but his wife insists that he must do the operation – such is her confidence in him. He reads up the operation in a textbook, and engages a local colleague to assist him. He bungles the operation and, as his wife lies in her bed, still convinced of her husband's brilliance, a senior surgeon comes finally to pronounce her dead.

The subtext of this story is deeply autobiographical, drawing on two events in Treves's own life: the failed blood transfusion upon the young woman in Wirksworth, and the failed operation upon his daughter Hetty. The narrative details of the cases are similar (the young and brilliant doctor in a country practice, the older colleague assisting, the inability of a senior surgeon to do anything). But what is more important is the moral Treves draws in 'The idol with hands of clay'. The young Treves's 'Anaemia treated by transfusion: a case of failure' provided a model of clear and courageous medical thinking. It was modest and it argued that one had to learn from failure rather than blunder on with vague diagnoses. It displayed a generous sensibility, remarkably free from vanity in a man of that age. By contrast, the lecture on appendicitis at Hammersmith in 1902 shows a crusty arrogance and a stubborn conservatism – a refusal to admit that others might be right, an insistence on doing it one's own way.

In 'The idol with hands of clay', the same issues are addressed, but there is a reversal: it is the *young* man who is arrogant. Unconsciously or not, Treves confronted these competing qualities in himself in the essay of 1923 – twenty years after Hetty's death. It is here that we may find Treves's account of what it was like to preside over the death of his daughter:

The young doctor told me that as he cut with his knife into that beautiful white skin and saw the blood well up behind it a lump rose in his throat and he felt that he must give up the venture. His vanity, however, urged him on. His doctor friend was watching him. He must impress him with his coolness and his mastery of the position. He talked of casual things to show that he was quite at ease, but his utterances were artificial and forced.

For a time all went well. He was showing off, he felt, with some effect. But when the depths of the wound were reached a condition of things was found which puzzled him. Structures were confused and matted together, and so obscured as to be unrecognizable. He had read of nothing like this in his books. It was the tenth case. He became uneasy and, indeed, alarmed, as one who had lost his way. He ceased to chatter. He tried to retain his attitude of coolness and command. He must be bold, he kept saying to himself. He made blind efforts to find his course, became wild and finally reckless. Then a terrible thing happened. There was a tear – something gave way – something gushed forth. His heart seemed to stop. He thought he should faint. A cold sweat broke out upon his brow. He ceased to speak. His trembling fingers groped aimlessly in the depths of the wound. His friend asked: 'What has happened?' He replied with a sickly fury: 'Shut up!'

He then tried to repair the damage he had done; took up instrument after instrument and dropped them again until the patient's body was covered with soiled and discarded forceps, knives and clamps. He wiped the sweat from his brow with his hand and left a wide streak of blood across his forehead. His knees shook and he stamped to try to stop them. He cursed the doctor who was helping him, crying out: 'For God's sake do this,' or 'For God's sake don't do that'; sighed like a suffocating man; looked appealingly to his wife's masked face for some sign of her tender comfort, but she was more than dumb. Frenzied with despair, he told the nurse to send for Mr Heron.... He tried again and again to close the awful rent, but he was now nearly dropping with terror and exhaustion. Then the anaesthetist said in a whisper: 'How much longer will you be? Her pulse is failing. She cannot stand much more.' He felt that he must finish or die. He finished in a way. He closed the wound, and then sank on a stool with his face buried in his blood-stained hands while the nurse and doctor applied the necessary dressing.

The patient was carried back to her bedroom, but he dared not follow. The doctor who had helped him crept away without speaking a word. He was left alone in this dreadful room with its hideous reminders of what he had done. He wandered about, looking aimlessly out of the window, but saw nothing, picked up his wife's handkerchief which was lying on the table, crunched it in his hand, and then dropped it on the floor as the red horror of it all flooded his brain. What had he done to her? She! She of all women in the world!

He caught sight of himself in the glass. His face was smeared with blood. He looked inhuman and unrecognizable. It was not himself he saw: it was a murderer with the brand of Cain upon his brow. He looked again at her handkerchief on the ground. It was the last thing her hand had closed upon. It was a piece of her lying amid this scene of unspeakable horror. It was like some ghastly item of evidence in a murder story. He could not touch it. He could not look at it. He covered it with a towel. . . . He told me that among the horrors that haunted him during these hours of waiting not the least were the flippant and callous thoughts that would force themselves into his mind with a fiendish brutality. There was, for example, a scent bottle on his wife's table – a present from her aunt. He found himself wondering why her aunt had given it to her and when, what she had paid for it, and what the aunt would say when she heard her niece was dead. Worse than that, he began composing in his mind an obituary notice for the newspapers. How should he word it? Should he say 'beloved wife,' or 'dearly loved wife,' and should he add all his medical qualifications? It was terrible. Terrible, too, was his constant longing to tell his wife of the trouble he was in and to be comforted by her.

Shortly after the surgeon left the anaesthetist noticed some momentary gleam of consciousness in the patient. The husband hurried in. The end had come. His wife's face was turned towards the window. The nurse lifted the blind a little so that the light fell upon her. She opened her eyes and at once recognized her husband. She tried to move her hand towards him, but it fell listless on the sheet. A smile – radiant, grateful, adoring – illumined her face, and as he bent over her he heard her whisper: 'Wonderful boy.'

(Treves 1923)

Chapter Six

EMINENCE

Treves was now a powerful force in medicine. When he wanted to ensure his influence, he generally worked behind the scenes rather than in a more public way. So while he served on the Royal College of Surgeons' court of examiners (1892–94) and on its council (1895–1903) he never sought to become its president.

While Treves could be a shrewd political operator, his outspokenness and impatience with mediocrity meant that he was often in conflict with colleagues, and this was aggravated by the fact that he enjoyed being at the centre of a political intrigue. One man who rubbed Treves up the wrong way was Henry Percy Dean, a young surgeon appointed to the London in 1892. Dean was a good surgeon, but he was also egotistical and flashy. The Spencers Wells forceps he used to treat private patients were gold plated. He owned two motor-cars, an unheard of luxury at that time. When called out on an emergency, he would drive one car himself, while his chauffeur followed in the other – in case one of them broke down, he would say with a smile.

Treves and Dean came into conflict when the younger man announced his plan to reorganize the teaching staff of the school. Apart from the fact that Treves saw reform as his area, Dean angered him by suggesting anatomy, physiology and pathology should be taught by new people brought in from outside the London. Dean believed that the London suffered from a kind of internal mafia, and that teaching would be improved if the monopoly were broken. Things came to a head when the demonstratorship in anatomy – Treves's old job – came up because of retirement. One of the outside applicants was Arthur Keith who had trained at Aberdeen, then done further work at Leipzig. Dean had already been instrumental in replacing one

London man on the staff, and now proposed to appoint Keith. In his history of the London, A. E. Clark-Kennedy sets the scene:

> the demonstratorship in anatomy fell vacant and Dean saw that it was advertised in the public press. Arthur Keith decided to apply. 'I soon learnt that the man to help me was Dean, but rivalry had sprung up between him and Treves, and I was warned that, if I was backed by Dean, I would be opposed by Treves.' And it worked out just like that. Dean was encouraging. 'I was deeply impressed by his manifest ability.' Treves was curt. The proper person to teach anatomy, he said, was the surgeon. Then, when Keith had lost all hope, he got a note from James Galloway, a friend of Treves and a graduate of Keith's own university of Aberdeen. Galloway had been getting at Treves and now wrote to suggest that Keith should call on him a second time. Again Treves was curt but this time agreed to support him. So Keith got the job, and his foothold in the medical college.
>
> (Clark-Kennedy 1963)

In his autobiography, Keith recounts how at the end of his first day at the London, the school held its annual welcome dinner for students. While he was wary of Treves, and smarting a bit from his initial reluctance to recommend him for a job, Keith understood right away what influence Treves held and why. He wrote in his autobiography:

> The chair was occupied by a physician of the hospital – Sir Stephen Mackenzie, brother of the more distinguished Sir Morel Mackenzie. I noticed that his audience listened with impatience to him when he discussed matters relating to needed improvements in medical education; on convivial occasions Englishmen do not want to hear about what is wrong with the world but what is already right in it. 'Freddy' Treves knew that. The moment he was on his feet all was expectation; his nimble wit soon restored merriment. Here again I was to see the social instrument used as an integrator. At these annual dinners old bonds were strengthened and new ones were formed; a living tradition was thus established in the life of the medical school.
>
> (Keith 1950)

But as far as Treves was concerned, Keith was an outsider who belonged to no London tradition. And, as his observation on the

English desire to be entertained rather than disturbed shows, Keith was very much a Scot. But Keith eventually became one of the most distinguished men on the staff of the London. Looking back, he wrote:

> It will be recalled that my first dealings with the great surgeon [Treves] were not of too friendly a nature, but by 1901, when he sometimes came to me for facts, his attitude, if it cannot be described as friendly, was quite civil. Treves had few intimate friends.

(Keith 1950)

While Treves could be sentimental in his writing, he rarely allowed his professional judgement to be clouded by positive or negative personal feelings. His criterion was, can the man do the job? As a consequence, though he had no special affection for Keith, Treves chose him as his collaborator in revising the fourth, fifth and sixth editions of *Surgical Applied Anatomy*. Keith offered sound skills which would ensure the book's integrity; in return, Treves offered fame and substantial royalty earnings.

By 1896 Treves's reputation was such that he was of real use in assisting the hospital in its fund-raising activities. Sydney Holland (later Viscount Knutsford) had developed the business of fund-raising to a fine art, and Treves became his chief lieutenant. Holland had a forceful style which appealed to Treves. He would coax, prod and shame in an effort to separate money from men, earning himself the nickname, 'the prince of beggars'. Treves would mount an early assault on the target, soften him up, and invite Holland in for the kill. An example of this involved a wealthy ex-patient of Treves's by the name of Fielden. Treves visited the man, explaining that the hospital needed funds for this and that, and would he discuss this with Holland? When Holland paid the visit, Fielden asked him to make a list, in his presence, of the hospital's needs. Holland wrote in his autobiography (Knutsford 1926), 'I started with £100 for something and went up to a complete isolation block costing £22,000'. A cheque for the entire list was written on the spot.

Between 1890 and 1895 Treves published four more books, including his first flop. This was *A German–English Dictionary of Medical Terms* (1890), written with Hugo Lang. Treves and his partner had spent five years reading 150 current German medical works and making a list of definitions for all important medical terms. Only when the reading was complete did the authors put the words into alphabetical order. The method was rather haphazard, and the book did not sell. More successful was Treves's massive two-volume work of 1891, *A Manual of Operative Surgery*, aimed at post-graduates and practitioners. Demand was so great that the publishers brought out an abridged version aimed at students preparing for examinations, *The Student's Handbook of Surgical Operations*. While it did not attain the classic status that *Surgical Applied Anatomy* did, it went through ten editions and twenty-seven printings between 1892 and 1957 both in Britain and in the US. His farewell to medical textbook writing was a two-volume work edited by him and published in 1895, *A System of Surgery*.

In this period Treves widened the scope of British surgery, devising and perfecting operations for conditions previously held to be either untreatable by surgery, or to be attended by very great risk to life. These included difficult hernias, gynaecological operations and cancer operations. But the conflict in Treves between radical and conservative approaches continued. Nowhere is this more evident than in his writings on Lister's antiseptic method as it applied practically to surgery. In 'A review of the surgery of the peritoneum' (1896), Treves took an iconoclastic view of Listerian procedure:

> It is no matter of great surprise that progress in the perfecting of the details of a great plan of treatment should have been at times erratic and ill-controlled. Since the days of the carbolic spray enthusiasts have rushed into strange and blundering extremes in their attempts to give practical expression to the dictum of 'strict antiseptic precautions'. These words have been with many a kind of mystic writing upon the wall, and activity in the interpretation of the message has been little short of confusion.
>
> (Treves 1896)

As with his rejection of the American notion of appendicitis, Treves dismisses 'continental' preoccupations with antiseptic conditions for surgery. The English method had to be best because it was 'practical'; European surgeons were to be ridiculed for their attention to detail:

> In this practical country we have been fortunately spared the extravagances which have brought certain Continental operating theatres into ridicule. Those who come after us will read with interest of the operating theatre built like a diving tank, of the glass table for the patient, of the exquisite ceremonial of washing

on the part of the operator, of the rites attending the ostentatious cleansing of the patient, of the surgeon in his robes of white mackintosh and his india-rubber fishing boots, and of the onlookers beyond the pale who are excluded with infinite solicitude, from the sacred circle as septic outlaws.

This exhibition may be scientific, but it is no part of surgery. It is more allied to a fervent idolatrous ritual brought down to the level of a popular performance. Those who have been led into these uncomfortable extravagances are no doubt honestly assured that they are carrying out the 'strictest antiseptic precautions', but in blindly effecting this end they appear to forget what is the prime purpose in the art of surgery. Can this extreme demonstration be necessary? Is it not piling Pelion on Ossas and slaying the already slain? The surgical ritualists appeal to the infallible tests of the bacteriological laboratory, and bring forth, as conclusive evidence, an array of cultivations and of innoculated tubes.

(Treves 1896)

But the 'absurd' continental ritual survived because it was correct practice. In ridiculing the importance of the 'bacteriological lab-oratory', Treves proclaims with a crude empiricism, 'Most English surgeons, on the other hand, are content to appeal to the test of the patient and to bring forth records of results'. This swashbuckling attitude later horrified Sir Philip Panton, who recalled in his autobi-ography how, as a student at Addenbrooke's at the time Treves was writing, he was called in by a famous surgeon to assist at an operation on a private patient.

[I] watched him trying to thread a needle with fine silk. Having some difficulty, he plunged his ungloved hand into his trouser pocket and produced his glasses. Still the thread would not go through, so he sucked it and finally succeeded in threading the needle. Before he plunged this filthy object into the patient's skin I ventured on a mild remonstrance, to get the crushing reply: 'Young man, when you have done as much surgery as I have, you will know just what you can get away with.' Whether this patient got away with it or not, I was never able to discover.

(Panton 1951)

Treves, of course, could mount impressive statistics – of his own making – to support his view: for instance, a record of 150 appendix operations during the 'quiescent' period with only one death (this, of course, ignores the statistic of how many lives were lost because surgery at the acute stage was avoided). Treves believed that 'when the feverish struggle of Continental surgeons to introduce mere novelties into surgical practice is at an end we may hope once more to resume the development of surgery as a handicraft'.

But here is another major contradiction. Treves insisted that surgery needed to be a science grounded in true anatomical principles; yet, at the same time, it had to be a handicraft, because surgery required 'a lacemaker's fingers and a seaman's grip'. Inexorably, the 'ridiculous' continental methods would become the standard practice of today. So what was Treves's own procedure?

In contradistinction to the vagaries of the new surgery, I would point out that a simple method, such as the following, appears sufficient to secure the much-exalted antiseptic precautions, or at least to produce admirable surgical results: The operating room is clean and free from dust. It may be in a hospital or it may be simply a wholesome bedroom in a private house. There is nothing peculiar in its construction. The table is of wood. It is not bacteriologically clean, but it is handy to the surgeon and comfortable to the patient – two points worthy of some consideration. Some time before the patient enters the theatre the skin of the abdomen is shaved, is well washed with soap and water and then with ether (or an ethereal solution of corrosive sublimate), and is finally covered by a thick compress soaked in a 1 in 20 carbolic solution, which is kept in position for at least five hours before the operation. The surgeon is clean, but he does not parade his cleanness. The mackintoshes and blankets which envelop the patient are, in a domestic sense, clean. The towels which cover the body in the vicinity of the operation area are taken direct from the steriliser. The instruments are sterilised by boiling, and are placed in a tray containing 1 in 20 carbolic acid solution. . . . Any onlookers who wish can approach the operation table, provided they touch neither patient, sponge, nor instrument. . . .

What dressings are used after operation is a matter of little or no moment. The wound is dried and well dusted with iodoform. The iodoform is kept in place by a pad of wool and a binder.

The selection of a dressing for a wound was at one time a matter
of infinite importance and anxious concern. It has now become a
question of not the least consequence. Many wounds require no
dressing at all. They are dried, dusted with iodoform, and are
left exposed to the air under the protection of a cradle. The fact
that the iodoform is swarming with micro-organisms may
disturb the bacterially-minded surgeon, but it disturbs neither
the wound nor the patient.

(Treves 1896)

Despite his quarrel with modernity (Treves would declare hateful
those Victorian railway stations now so beloved of conservationists),
he was the leader of his profession in Britain. But, in 1898 – aged only
forty-five, and having done twenty years at the London – Treves
decided to retire from the London. Among his generation he had been
first to qualify as a member and then fellow of the RCP, first to be
appointed a consultant and, now, first to retire. Moderation was
never his strong point. While Treves was never flamboyant, he stood
out as someone who made his own way. He was unconventional.

Upon his retirement Treves reflected that surgery had been trans-
formed in his lifetime, and that one of the major changes was that
'where there was one surgeon there are now ten'. The swashbuckling
operator of crude brilliance was replaced by an army of sober men
working confidently in the abdomen, the chest, even the brain. Part of
his reason for early retirement can be found here, because Treves now
saw surgery as a growing 'democratic' movement, greater than any
individual talent. One surgeon would step aside to be replaced by
another. 'The democratic movement is the active power of the day,
and that an oligarchy in the community of surgeons should be replaced by an earnest democracy is precisely in accord with the spirit
of the times.' In a moment of genuine modesty, Treves put his own
eminence in perspective:

Advance in such a work as ours depends upon the uneventful
work of the whole body and is only accentuated by achievements
of the prominent few. The movement is the movement of a
multitude in which individuality is, at a distance of time, little to
be distinguished and in which personal eminence contributes a
smaller factor than the present is ready to acknowledge. Those
who stand forth as the leaders of the advance are merely the
elect of the common body and are the representatives of a wide

intellectual franchise. Even he who startles the world as a discoverer has often done little more than give expression to what was already nascent in the multitude. So as one great surgeon after another drops out of the ranks his place is rapidly and imperceptibly filled, and the advancing line moves on with still the same solid and unbroken front.

(Treves 1897)

Part of Treves's motive in retiring early was to create a place which a new generation of ambitious young men could compete to fill; but the hard work of teaching, surgery and extra-curricular activities had also taken their toll. Treves was now, if not wealthy, very comfortably off. He was a man of wide interests, and he intended to pursue them.

But Treves was not retiring altogether; he would still keep his private practice. On learning of his retirement, the *British Medical Journal* commented:

The retirement of Mr Treves six years before the expiration of his term of office will be a loss to the hospital and medical school in connection with which his early reputation was made; but we understand that he found the claims of private practice incompatible with the exacting duties of surgeon to a large hospital.

More candidly, W. R. Bett remarked that Treves's 'private practice became so embarrassingly extensive that he resigned the post of surgeon to the London Hospital in 1898, at the age of forty-five – a step undoubtedly to his financial advantage' (Bett 1953). More than any other surgeon of his day, Treves regularly commanded the maximum fee of 100 guineas.

But the advantages of retirement were offset by liabilities, chief among them the fact that a surgeon needed a hospital in order to stay at the forefront. That great biographer of surgeons, Victor Plarr, shrewdly observed that 'Treves as Surgeon to the London Hospital was recognized as the leader of English surgery. After his resignation, he gradually ceased to lead' (Plarr 1930). But leadership in surgery was no longer enough for Treves. He hungered for adventure and for influence.

Chapter Seven

WAR

At tea time on 11 October 1899 the Boer War (or Great Anglo-Boer War) began. Surgeons would be needed. Treves made up his mind to go.

In November the Duchess of Bedford put a large sum at Treves's disposal to put together his own surgical team to follow Buller's army in Natal. Though he was appointed Consulting Surgeon with the Field Force, Treves's enterprise was private. It was a most unusual state of affairs. Instead of accepting the usual army issue male nurses, Treves brought two female ones – Alice Tarr and Ethel McCaul – from the London. He designed his own surgical kit rather than use the one provided by the RAMC; and when he arrived in South Africa he employed his own servants and transport.

Treves was already famous within his profession, so it was not surprising when, two days before his departure, the *British Medical Journal* carried a full report, down to the smallest detail, on his preparations for war. But the publicity surrounding Merrick's case had brought him wider fame, and the popular press carried big stories on his departure. On Friday 10 November 1899, the Prince of Wales invited Treves to Marlborough House to wish him well. The future king hoped that Treves's experience of war would lead to important contributions in military medicine.

On the Saturday at eleven a.m. a crowd of nearly four hundred medical students from the London, St Mary's, and University College Hospital thronged the platform of Waterloo Station to say good-bye. Treves arrived at 11.15 and was met by a great cheer. The students hoisted him onto their shoulders and carried him to his train. *The Times* correspondent wrote that 'This incident reminded one irresistibly of the rush of forwards on the football field, and the mighty cheer that went up, as Mr Treves was safely landed at his carriage door, suggested the cheer which rises when the ball has been carried behind the goal'. The crowd was so enthusiastic that police were called by railway officials anxious to maintain order. And when Treves was settled in his carriage he found it overflowing with flowers sent by well-wishers.

In the twenty minutes that Treves waited for the train to pull out, the cheering crowd swelled. As he leaned from the window shaking hands with nurses, students, and colleagues, and saying goodbye to family and friends, the crowd broke into choruses of 'Rule Britannia' and 'For He's a Jolly Good Fellow'. They demanded a speech. Treves replied: 'My dear boys, it is quite impossible for me to thank you adequately for this very kind send-off. You know my attachment to the old hospital, and to see such a body of old London Hospital men here touches me very deeply. Nothing in my professional career has given me greater joy.' It was a sentimental morning: the students now sang 'Auld Lang Syne' and 'God Save the Queen'.

Though Treves was the immediate focus of this feeling, he was not the source of it. England was in the grip of a fervent patriotism, exhilarated by the prospect of what was expected to be a short and victorious war in South Africa. Treves's farewell scene was one of many which would be enacted at Waterloo over the coming months. The singing and cheering crowd thought of pride and glory. They didn't think of death and destruction.

Later that afternoon Treves boarded the *Dunvegan Castle* for the long sea journey. South Africa was to be a turning point in his life.

*   *   *

Treves was attached to the army under Sir Redvers Buller, and was present at all of the disastrous engagements leading up to the relief of Ladysmith. He was part of a team comprising the Number 4 Field Hospital which followed the army at the battles of Colenso, Spion Kop and Spearman's Hill, and which handled virtually all of the wounded from these engagements. Treves wrote regular letters from the front which were published jointly by the *Lancet* and the *British Medical Journal* (these would form the basis for his first popular book, *The Tale of a Field Hospital* (1900)).

When Treves arrived at Frere Camp on the Tugela River on 11 December, the heat was unbearable. What made life (and surgery)

particularly difficult was the lack of clean water. It 'was the colour
peasoup, and when in a glass was semi-opaque and of a faint brown-
ish colour. It soon blocked a Berkefeld filter, the pencil of which had to
be cleaned after each water bottle had been pumped full.' There were
30,000 men under canvas at Frere, and Treves's first reaction was to
marvel at the strange beauty of it. Like all visitors to southern Africa
he was affected by the intensity of light and colour: blue sky, red earth.
On the day he arrived, his writing had the quality of a travel book.
Two days later the army moved out. The tone of his writing changed
overnight. His war was beginning.

As the column moved out Treves

> could see the firing of the great naval guns and the clouds of dust
> sent up by the exploding shells, and now and then from the
> weary road would come an attenuated sound, which was all that
> reached us of the shrill yells of the nigger drivers, whose dust-
> dried throats gave out noises like the shrieks of parrots.
>
> (Treves 1900)

On the morning of Friday 15 December the battle of Colenso began.
Number 4 Field Hospital was stationed three and three-quarter miles
from Naval Hill, on which the English had pitched their large guns.
As soon as he arrived, Treves was sent down to the front.

> The scene presented at this spot was beyond description. The
> men were coming in as fast as the ambulance bearers could
> bring them. Some were dead, some were dying, all were parched
> with thirst and baked and blistered with heat. The men were
> lying on all sides on stretchers – amidst tents, piles of rifles,
> accoutrements, battered helmets, and blood-stained tunics. It
> was a sight no one would wish to see again, and the blazing sun
> added to the miseries of all.
>
> (Treves 1900)

After Colenso eight hundred wounded passed through the four field
hospitals to be dealt with by sixteen surgeons; but each field hospital
was designed to deal with a maximum of one hundred patients at a
time. In writing to his medical audience at home, Treves decided to
praise the army arrangements, despite their shortcomings.

> Those who harshly criticize the Army Medical Department
> should have seen the work done on that memorable Friday on
> the Naval Hill before Colenso. No work could have been done

better. The equipment was good, the arrangements elaborated, and the officers worked on hour after hour without rest or food under the most trying possible conditions. No greater strain could have fallen upon a department and all concerned met the brunt of it valiantly and well. One could not be other than proud of one's profession.

(Treves 1900)

But Treves's true feelings were mixed, and his letters cannot hide his criticism. While patriotically praising his army colleagues, he noted that: 'Our hospital at Chieveley was crammed to its utmost, and very many wounded men had to lie all night in the open. Fortunately the nights on Friday and Saturday were very fine, and there was a bright moon.'

Surgery at the front was a primitive business. In the absence of operating tables, stacked biscuit boxes were used. The surgical tents swarmed with flies and the water was filthy. There were great queues of wounded men outside the tents who had to endure their own agonies while listening to the cries of others. Morphia and chloroform were not administered until the patient was on the 'table'.

The scene inside the tent was terrible. Treves wrote:

One instance of the limited capacity of the marquee I may be pardoned for recounting. The amputation of a leg was in progress when the pressure of work was at its height. Beneath the table at the time of the operation was the prostrate figure of a man. He had been shot through the face. His big moustache was clotted with blood, his features were obliterated by dust and blood, his eyes were shut, and his head generally was enveloped in bandages. I thought he was dead, and that in the hurry of events he was merely awaiting removal. The limb after amputation was unfortunately dropped upon this apparently inanimate figure when, to my horror, the head was raised and the eyes were opened to ascertain the nature of the falling body. This poor fellow was attended to as soon as the table was free. I was glad to see him some weeks after in the Assembly Hotel at Pietermaritzburg, hearty and well. He was a gallant officer in a Natal regiment, and when I recalled this gruesome incident to him, he owned that, feeble as he was at the time, it gave him a 'shake up'.

(Treves 1900)

Amidst the chaos of Colenso there was no time for the personal relationship with patients that Treves was used to in London. The dead were set to one side, judgements made about the wounded, and those cases selected for operation who had some chance of survival. The war became personal for Treves when Field Marshal Lord Roberts's son, Lieutenant Frederick Sherston Roberts, was brought back mortally wounded.

After a heavy afternoon on the field I returned to Chieveley Field Hospital in the evening, but had barely got in when a galloper arrived to ask me to see Lieutenant Roberts, who had just been brought back. I returned at once with a full equipment of instruments, and much regret that that valiant soldier was from the first quite beyond the reach of surgery. In addition to a penetrating wound of the abdomen, his forearm was shattered by a Mauser and his knee wounded by a shell. He was pulseless. I slept outside his tent that night, and saw him up to Chieveley on Saturday morning. He never rallied nor regained his pulse, and died on Saturday at midnight.

(Treves 1900)

Later Treves told the full story to Sir Newman Flower:

'Roberts was dying that night,' Treves told me, 'and he did not know what sort of a world he was going to. He believed that there was another life. In a vague way he felt sure of it. But his mind in turmoil could not fashion this next life. What did I think of it? Was there another life after all? He felt that there must be.

'I sat outside his tent all through the long hours of night discussing things like that with him. We talked through the half-open flap of the tent. There *was* another life. I made that quite clear to his mind during those moments which swayed him this way and that in belief. There *is* another life, and I told him I knew there was. We talked in this fashion – cross-examining each other – through the flap of that tent throughout the hours. The shadows of the African dusk seemed to bring us together. We were not two people who had met; we were just two pals who were talking about the future to which each and both would some day go. Young Roberts passed out as we were talking . . .

'On the Christmas after he died, I went up to the grave where

89

we had buried him. I took with me some flowers to lay to his memory on behalf of his family. To my amazement I found that the hot earth had drawn the body completely out of the ground. He lay there a stark corpse upon the earth. And I buried him again myself, reverently and carefully, deeper and deeper, beyond the heat of the sun. And no one ever knew. . . .'

(Flower 1950)

While Treves witnessed a great deal of tragedy, the war also provided some comic moments. This one is also told by Newman Flower:

After the battle [of Colenso] a certain Major, who had been badly shot, passed through his hands. Treves put him in the train and made him as comfortable as he could. He had been a cheerful fellow under pain, and had shown abnormal courage under extreme hurt. Treves placed a bottle of water beside him and said: 'You can take a mouthful of water every hour. If you drink more, nothing on earth will save you; you will die. Goodbye and good luck.'

Two years before Treves and I sat on the Vevey bench a man came up to him in London and said:

'You don't remember me?'

'No,' said Treves, 'I don't.'

'I'm Major —. You remember the bottle of water after Colenso?'

'Of course I do,' said Treves. 'And I'm very glad you obeyed orders.'

'But I didn't. I drank the whole bloody lot just as soon as you left the train. I couldn't help it!'

(Flower 1950)

On Sunday 17 December the Boer shells were landing perilously close to Chieveley Field Hospital and Treves and his colleagues were forced to retreat to the previous camp at Frere. The temperature had climbed to 104° in the shade. There was no water. More than eight hundred men were wounded at Colenso. They all had to be moved. Partly to console himself, perhaps, Treves wrote this untruth to the medical journals at home: 'Those in England who have friends among the army in Natal may rest assured that the wounded are well looked after, and that the arrangements for their comfort leave little to be desired' (Treves 1900). The medical teams did what they could; but the crude transport arrangements killed scores of wounded who should have survived, and the field hospitals lacked the facilities to ensure their proper treatment, never mind comfort. On this black Sunday Treves diverted himself by reflecting on the capriciousness of the Mauser bullet.

> In several instances the bullet has passed through the brain without causing marked symptoms, and perfect recovery has followed. For example, a bullet entered near the vertex, passed through the brain, hard palate, and buccal cavity, and escaped at the root of the neck on the opposite side. No discomfort followed except headache and some strabismus.
>
> (Treves 1900)

The medical problems in Natal were largely the outcome of military management – or lack of it. When Treves arrived in South Africa Buller's task was the relief of Ladysmith, and he had already suffered defeats at Stormberg and Magersfontein. To relieve Ladysmith Buller needed to cross the Tugela River. After Colenso he made the attempt; but he was to be thwarted at Spion Kop and Vaal Krantz.

Colenso was probably lost before the British made their first move. Buller's opposite number, Botha, was expecting a frontal attack, and that is precisely what the British did. In his haste to relieve Ladysmith Buller was incautious, and his men were unprepared. Orders were not issued until midnight of the evening preceding Colenso, and officers were very unsure of the terrain. They had to work from crude one-inch maps based on farm surveys which lacked contours.

At Colenso the British were in trouble from the start. Major-General Hart's flank crumbled immediately – not surprising, perhaps, given the fact that he subjected his Irish Brigade to an hour's parade ground drill in the sweltering heat just before mounting his attack. Misled by his guide, Hart marched his troops straight into the Boer guns in close formation. Only the good sense of the men – those who survived the initial volleys broke ranks and ran for cover – prevented a total massacre.

Hart was not the only one to make a fatal error. Colonel Long's guns were placed closer than Buller had instructed, and they were captured by the Boers with the loss of several officers and men. Buller himself showed personal bravery on the field, but had to admit defeat. He withdrew.

The cost was high: 143 British killed and 996 wounded. The Boers

lost only eight men, with thirty wounded. As Byron Farwell laconi-
cally notes, these were 'heavy casualties for a battle in which neither
side attacked' (Farwell 1977). In addition to the human casualties,
Buller lost a total of ten guns. 'To lose one gun was a disgrace. To lose
ten of them – and without a single one of the enemy actually ever
touching them until they hauled them away – was unthinkable.' After
Colenso, Treves praises the men and maintains that morale continues
to be high. But it was patriotic wishful thinking rather than fact. For,
as Farwell points out, Buller's leadership had collapsed, and this
affected the troops:

> Buller could hardly face the enormity of his failure; he blamed
> Hart and particularly Long. But the fault lay not with others,
> but with himself. He was a Victorian Hamlet, wanting action,
> provoking it, yet afraid of the consequences of acting on his own
> judgement. He did not, like Hamlet, contemplate suicide, but he
> did that which for a general is worse: he expressed his conviction
> that he could not win. He advised the War Office that he
> considered himself incapable of relieving Ladysmith, and he sent
> off two extraordinary messages by helio to White in the besieged
> town saying, 'The enemy is too strong for my force . . . I cannot
> break in', and suggesting that he fire off as much ammunition as
> he could, destroy his cypher books, and make the best terms
> possible with the Boers. White could not believe the message was
> genuine. He thought the Boers had sent it. When it was
> confirmed he signalled back: 'The loss of 12,000 men here would
> be a heavy blow to England. We must not think of it.'
>
> (Farwell 1977)

After Colenso, Buller re-established his headquarters at Frere. By
now the wounded had been dealt with by the surgeons, but the real
killer of the Boer War appeared: disease.

> We soon became filled up with cases of dysentery and enteric
> fever. The dysentery was of a severe type, and we had several
> deaths. One of my nurses (Miss Tarr) was, I am sorry to say,
> taken ill with dysentery, and was removed at once to Martizburg
> [sic]. She developed the affection in a very acute form, and at
> one time her life was despaired of. She is now, I hear, doing well,
> but will, of course, not be able to go to the front again.
>
> (Treves 1900)

Only one private communication from Treves in South Africa survives – a postcard to his brother William in Margate. Dated 21 December 1899, its tone is more realistic than the letters to the medical press, but it shows Treves to be in good spirits:

> I was present at the battle of the Tugela River (opposite Colenso) on Dec. 15. It was a pretty horrid business and beyond description. We had 800 wounded through the Field Hospital on Friday and Sat: and as the Boer shells could reach us at Chievly [sic] we moved back to Frere on Sunday. The heat is intense and as we are on the open veld there is absolutely no shade of any kind. The temp. has been at 100 to 105 in the shade and as there is little water we have all had a bad time from thirst. A clinical thermometer left in a leather bag in the shade of a tent registered 105.4. This has been no picnic and pretty hard work. Grub is hard to get and 'bully beef' does not grow on one. We are all very fit and of course burnt black. I am going to the front again with the Cavalry Brigade. The nurses will remain at Frere with the Stationary Field Hosp. and move on in the rear of the column. The water at Frere is the colour pea soup and there is much dysentery. But for the heat – which is now less – the climate is charming. A pleasant Christmas to all at Dalby Square. I shall probably spend my Xmas on the veld about Springfield. No one knows when the next move is to take place.

Almost a month after Colenso, on 12 January 1900, Buller left Frere and began his march to Springfield, some eighteen miles away. The field hospitals moved on the following day. In anticipation of a large battle on or near the Tugela, Treves's Number 4 Stationary Field Hospital was redesignated a mobile unit which would follow the troops. It had to: otherwise all the wounded would have to be carried back to Frere. The Principal Medical Officer, Colonel Gallwey, set up a general hospital at Mooi River with 500 beds. There were a further 1,000 beds available at Martizburg (Pietermaritzburg) and a few at Estcourt. Treves enthused: 'There can be no doubt that Colonel Gallwey's arrangements were ably conceived and admirably carried out. He certainly spared no trouble to make the Army Medical Department in Natal a complete success' (Treves 1900).

Treves described the new look field hospital which marched to the Tugela.

The hospital is to accommodate a minimum of 300 beds, and was made up of 60 tents and 10 marquees. The rank and file of the R.A.M.C. numbered 88. There were 12 surgeons including myself, 2 army sisters, and my remaining nurse Miss McCaul. We also took with us 100 coolies for camp work, who walked all the way with their earthly possessions on their heads. Our train was composed of 16 ox waggons each with 16 oxen. The water and bread carts were also drawn by oxen, so that the number of oxen employed was over 260. There were 5 ambulances, each drawn by 10 mules. My own transport consisted of a small covered waggon, a Scotch cart, 16 mules, a conductor on horseback, 4 Kaffir 'boys', a groom, and my manservant. There were therefore 66 mules on the road. I rode on horseback, as did most of the other surgeons.

(Treves 1900)

The company rose at three a.m., reaching Springfield at two-thirty in the afternoon.

At Springfield preparations for a great battle began. Treves noted the stark contrast between the reality of the battle that lay before them, and the natural beauty of the Natal landscape. It was an eerie scene:

I rode each day to the hill commanding the Great Tugela upon which our big guns are placed. The view from this hill is grand in the extreme. It commands a splendid plain covered with kopjes, across which runs the Ladysmith road. At the bottom of the hill, which was rendered beautiful by mimosa trees in bloom, was the drift. The Boer trenches were well in view, and until our big guns began I could see the Boers working in their shirtsleeves at their all-pervading earthworks.

(Treves 1900)

Five days later, on Thursday 18 January, the field hospital moved six miles forward to the banks of the river. As the day of battle approached, Treves noted that 'There was a suspiciously large number of Boer ambulances to be seen, and I imagine that not a few of them were carrying ammunition and supplies' (Treves 1900). Whether they were or not, the fantasy could be fuelled by the fact that the British were dangerously short of supplies of every description. If Treves's exaggerated praise of the RAMC provision at Colenso is anything to go by, then this slightly glum description of the scene at the Tugela hides a nightmare: 'The soldiers have been lying out without tents and on short rations, but fortunately the weather has been fine.... The transport of rations, fodder, and ammunition for the large force employed must tax the Army Service Corps to the utmost' (Treves 1900).

With Number 4 Field Hospital set up, the plan was for the wounded to be brought there first, then on to Frere and, finally, to the base hospital twenty-five miles from Frere. 'The road is not so bad as roads go in this part of the country,' Treves wrote cautiously; but 'it is very rough in places, and several drifts have to be crossed' (Treves 1900).

The battle began and the wounded started to arrive at Number 4 Field Hospital on Sunday 21 January. Most were from Sir Charles Warren's division – a curious soldier who thought troops should be 'introduced' to the enemy before fighting them through a 'dress rehearsal'. He had a fatal belief in the utility of oxen, and amused his men by tending the beasts himself. Oxen had the virtue of being strong; but they were also slow. Warren's troops moved from their camp near Springfield on the evening of 16 January. 'Although it was called a flying column,' wrote one historian, 'Warren's force, with its thousands of oxen and its laden wagons, was about as dashing as a centipede.'

Warren's 'flying column' consisted of thirty-six field guns, three brigades and 1,500 mounted men. Buller's plan was for Warren to cross the Tugela at Trenchard's Drift and so attack the Boer positions. Having reached Trenchard's Drift at midnight, Warren decided not to cross (though Farwell points out that 'infantry and light cavalry could have crossed without a bridge' [Farwell 1977]). At this point 500 Boers were waiting on the other side. In the morning Warren built a pontoon bridge and watched the leisurely crossing of beasts and men. The next day he marched his army another three miles in, his every move being observed by the Boer scouts. The Boers began to build defences and to call in reinforcements. The Earl of Dundonald, who was to guard Warren's left flank, ambushed a 300-man Boer commando. In their elation at this small victory, the British did not realize that they could easily have relieved Ladysmith from their present position.

Warren held off his attack until 20 January, giving the Boers ample time to prepare. By now the Boers were in a position of such overwhelming superiority that all British advances had to be made across open country. In a tentative move forward, twenty-eight of Warren's officers and men were killed and 280 wounded. Warren did not have to wait for history to judge him harshly. As soon as the army reached Ladysmith, Buller relieved him of his command. Farwell argues that the severe losses the British were about to suffer at Spion Kop were due mainly to incompetence and negligence:

> Buller's mistakes were those of a simple, honest soldier, determined to do his duty but thrust into a position where he was expected to assume more responsibility than he wanted or could handle. Failure resulted from his lack of skill in planning battles involving large bodies of men, his own awareness of his deficiencies (though he tried to hide them from others), and his deep compassion for those he led, which he concealed behind a gruff, uncommunicative manner. Warren's mistakes were those of an arrogant man caught in the net of his own absurd theories and deceived by his own conceit. He hid his lack of experience, his uncertainty, and his lack of ability behind a mask of bouncing self-confidence. Buller was a blunderer, but Warren was a fool.
>
> (Farwell 1977)

The indecisive pair of Buller and Warren settled on Spion Kop as the site of the battle. From Sunday 21 January Warren's wounded had been arriving at Number 4 Field Hospital at the rate of between fifty and 150 men per day. As they continued to straggle in, the attack on Spion Kop commenced early on Wednesday 24 January. Treves wrote:

> I was awakened about 3 a.m. by the rifle fire attending the night attack upon the hill, and all through the day the artillery and rifle fire was terrible and incessant. Spion Kop is just opposite the hill under the shelter of which our hospital stands, and from this hill the engagement could be witnessed. The hill is steep, and was approached from the side of the river. I watched our men climb up, and it was evident that in certain steep places the getting of the wounded down would be attended with difficulty. The shell fire to which our men were subjected was very severe, and it was clear that the casualties would be numerous.
>
> (Treves, 1900)

When the field hospital had arrived at the Tugela it comprised sixty tents and ten marquees. On Tuesday 23 January, the day before the battle, a further 100 bell tents were ordered. These could accommodate a further 500 wounded. But no extra medical or nursing staff were available.

On Thursday 25 January the wounded from Spion Kop began to pour in. On the first day of the battle some 300 men were treated at Number 4 Field Hospital. Later that day a further 600 wounded were brought down. While 900 wounded were now in the field hospital – equipped to deal with only a fraction of that number – Treves wrote that 'The larger number of the wounded were on the top of Spion Kop'. In his account to the medical press, Treves coolly described the horror of the battle.

> The path down was about two miles, was steep, and in places very difficult. The carriage of the wounded down the hill had all to be by hand. From the foot of the hill to the hospital the carriage was by ambulance waggons and in some cases by coolie bearers. All the stretchers had hoods. There was no doubt that the wounded suffered very much on account of the tedious transport, but it was rendered as nearly perfect as possible. . . . The surgeons who went after the wounded on the top of the hill told me that the sight of the dead and injured was terrible in the extreme, the wounds having been mostly from shell and shrapnel; some men had been blown almost to pieces.
>
> (Treves 1900)

Poor leadership and appalling conditions made the ordinary soldier's lot exceedingly miserable. Most of the men had not had a change of clothes for ten days. Most had to sleep in the open, facing a cold night without greatcoats after a blistering day. They were on short rations and facing an incredible test of physical endurance as the battle was fought on such steep terrain. And the incessant noise of shells and gunfire made rest impossible. Working its way insidiously into the mind, it took a heavy psychological toll. A patriot to the last – but an increasingly disillusioned one – Treves wrote:

> In spite of all their hardships the wounded men behaved as splendidly as they have always done. They never complained. . . .

The English soldier is a man of whom the country may well be proud, and in these two terrible engagements on the Tugela they behaved from first to last in a manner worthy of the splendid traditions of the British Army.

(Treves 1900)

For all his bluff, Treves partially acknowledged the total mess the British had made to date of a war which was to be 'over by Christmas' and which mounted the full might of the British army against a 'rabble' force of untrained Boer farmers: the men 'were much depressed at the reverse', he admitted. The incident which affected Treves most at this juncture was the following:

One poor fellow had been shot in the face by a piece of shell, which had carried away his left eye, the left upper jaw with the corresponding part of the cheek, and had left a hideous cavity at the bottom of which his tongue was exposed. He had been lying hours on the hill. He was unable to speak, and as soon as he was landed at the hospital he made signs that he wanted to write. Pencil and paper were given him, and it was supposed he wished to ask for something, but he merely wrote, 'Did we win?'. No one had the heart to tell him the truth.

(Treves 1900)

The numbers of British dead and wounded were horrific; according to Selby, 1,750.

The experience of one young English journalist during the battle of Spion Kop underlines the tragedy of the event. He observed that

Sir Redvers Buller said little, and what he said was obscure. He was a man of considerable scale. He plodded from blunder to blunder and from one disaster to another, without losing either the regard of his country or the trust of his troops, to whose feeling as well as his own he paid serious attention.

The journalist was Winston Churchill. Observing the battle at close quarters, Churchill could see the disaster which was about to occur. Finding himself standing behind the incompetent Warren he made so bold as to offer advice. Warren promptly had him arrested.

*   *   *

After Spion Kop the army retired to Chieveley Camp where Treves

98

was laid low with dysentery. The surgeons faced a new problem of suppurating shell wounds, of which they had little experience. This caused 'simpler wounds which would, under ordinary circumstances, have healed without any trouble' to become infected. From 15 February to 1 March 'there was fighting every day and all day', Treves wrote. The medical staff was depleted through dysentery and there were not enough stretcher bearers. The wounded 'were often lying out for some time before they could be reached by the stretcher-bearers. Thus, many were lying out all night, and one man I talked to was unfortunately out two nights and a day' (Treves 1900). The Boers were now using exploding dum dum bullets which caused terrible injuries – a small wound at the point of entry and a gaping hole at the point of exit.

Finally, on 27 February, there was a breakthrough. The British stormed Pieter's Hill, opening the way to Ladysmith. Treves was jubilant.

> Late on the afternoon of February 27th we were able to view from our camp at Chieveley the grandest spectacle of this campaign – the storming of Pieter's Hill. The hill formed a long ridge, or series of ridges, immediately in front of Umbulwana. The afternoon was a little cloudy, but a wide patch of sunshine rested upon this fateful ridge and made it luminous against the gloomy walls of Umbulwana. A more terrific display of artillery fire could hardly be imagined. It was incessant. The sound was as the roar of some uncanny sea. The air above the ridge was alive with the little white clouds of shrapnel, and on the ground itself were flashing lyddite and common shell and brown columns of dust, which rose up and were made brilliant by the sun. When the artillery ceased the rifle fire could be heard, and later on we knew that the trenches had been taken at the point of the bayonet, and that the way to Ladysmith was open.
>
> (Treves 1900)

The cavalry reached Ladysmith around six p.m. on Wednesday 28 February. Buller arrived the following day, and on Friday Treves and the rest of the field hospital staff entered the besieged garrison. The journey was difficult as the main road was not yet secure, and Treves had to make his way over rough country in the army's wake. He travelled in his covered cart (known in the camp as 'the bus') with Ethel McCaul and an army chaplain. His caravan included ten mules, two Africans and a servant 'who rode in front to pick out the road'.

They left Chieveley at six-thirty in the morning, equipped with two days' provisions for the twenty-three mile journey. Crossing the battlefield at Colenso, Treves 'came across the skeletons of Colonel Long's horses attached to the lost guns; they were lying in a line as they fell, their bones were whitened, but still attached to them were the collars and harness' (Treves 1900). From a hill overlooking the Tugela Treves could see a mighty convoy of ox wagons bringing supplies to Ladysmith, followed by a sorry parade of stragglers. The journey was difficult, and Treves and his party arrived tired and shaken at two-thirty in the afternoon. From a distance, it was impossible to imagine the misery of the place. Ladysmith looked charming:

> At last on mounting the summit of a little ridge we saw before us a wide green plain of waving grass, and beyond the plain and under the shelter of purple hills lay the unhappy town of Ladysmith. Ladysmith looks very pretty at the distance – a cluster of white and red roofs dotted among trees, and surmounted by the white tower of the town hall.
>
> (Treves 1900)

Treves arrived four hours before the supply train and he witnessed the appalling conditions of the 12,000 British. Entering the camp of the King's Royal Rifles, the men 'were piteous to see. They were thin and hollow-eyed, and had about them an air of utter lassitude and weariness. Some were greatly emaciated, nearly all were pale, nearly all were silent. They exhausted every topic of discussion, it would seem, and were too feeble to discuss even their relief' (Treves 1900). Having no tents, the soldiers had made shelters on the side of a hill using stones and bits of wood and wire. Some had burrowed into the ground, and Treves remarked that it was if they 'had returned to the type of habitation common to primeval man'. Treves had no food to give the soldiers, but they gratefully accepted all the tobacco he had, which he doled out in pipesful. Leaving the camp, Treves was approached by 'a skeleton of a Kaffir, who offered me a shilling, while he pointed repeatedly to his mouth. He was really starving, and devoured the biscuits I gave him like a wolf.' He remarked, 'There is no doubt that the coloured people left in Ladysmith have suffered very greatly'. He was greatly affected by an incident which occurred on leaving the town. He was accosted by a Scot in charge of an ox wagon, who asked if he 'knew anything of doctoring'. One of the Scot's African servants had been run over by a wagon and had four broken ribs. Treves looked about for a makeshift bandage with which to bind the injured man's ribs and could find nothing. The Scot took off his own shirt and ripped it into strips – even though it meant enduring a cold night in the open.

Treves left Ladysmith at five p.m. Reaching the Tugela at nightfall, he spent a sleepless night under the stars before resuming his journey. The next day his wagon broke down while fording the river. Treves and his party made their way along the railway line to Colenso on the backs of the mules. 'The line took us through a district where fighting had been very heavy, and we were all the way sickened by the hideous smell of numerous dead horses and of still more numerous dead and imperfectly buried Boers' (Treves 1900). Rough British graves could be seen everywhere on either side of the line, interspersed with the rubbish of war: cartridge cases, abandoned ammunition, empty ration tins.

Returning to Chieveley Treves was taken ill with dysentery and sent to Durban to recover. Within a week he was sailing for England. The war in South Africa was over for him. But another one was about to begin at home.

Chapter Eight

SCANDAL

Q. In fact you were not aware of any serious cause of complaint in the course of the campaign?
A. We met with none.
Treves in evidence to the 1900 Royal Commission on the Care of the Sick and Wounded During the South African Campaign

The military hospitals do not come up to the standards of a workhouse infirmary.
Treves in evidence to the 1903 Royal Commission on the War in South Africa

The medical arrangements have been everything that could be desired. I am sure that I only express the feelings of the whole force when I say that every one is grateful to Sir William McCormac [sic], Mr. Treves, and Sir William Stokes, whose skill has saved several lives and mitigated much suffering, and whose knowledge and experience have been a blessing to the sick and wounded.
General Sir Redvers Buller in a despatch of 30 March 1900

Treves returned to a hero's welcome. But there was mounting criticism at home of the Royal Army Medical Corp's performance in South Africa, and *The Times* made it a campaigning issue. On 28 April 1900 Lord Rosebery gave a dinner for Treves and Sir William Mac-Cormack at the Reform Club. In a toast to the guests of honour, Rosebery contradicted the facts when he bluffly proclaimed that 'in a war in which there has been so much correspondence as this, and therefore so much diversity of opinion, there has been unanimity only on one point, and enthusiastic unanimity – that our medical and hospital service have been practically perfect'. Treves replied by saying that 'there had never been a campaign in which the horrors of war had been so mitigated, and when the treatment of the wounded had been so complete'. He said the experience made him 'proud to be an Englishman, and proud to be a surgeon'.

The whole evening was a crude public relations stunt designed to contradict accurate press reports and maintain flagging public support for the war. While Treves might have been proud to be an Englishman, the Reform Club dinner was a stunning example of English stupidity and arrogance.

On 2 May *The Times* published a leading article which was highly critical of the RAMC. Despite his public support of the army in South Africa, Treves and MacCormack, knowing the truth, decided to write a letter to the editor distancing themselves from the RAMC:

> In the remarks contained in your leading article of this morning it would appear as if the consulting surgeons attached to the field force in South Africa had been concerned in organising the medical arrangements of the campaign. This was no part of their duty, which was solely to afford professional advice and assistance as consultants to the Army Medical officers. In the exercise of these duties they have been happily able to testify to the admirable and effective organisation of the medical department of the Army for which the officers of the medical service are alone responsible.
>
> (Treves and MacCormack 1900)

The Times's leader was inspired by reports from its special correspondent in South Africa, William Burdett-Coutts. Burdett-Coutts was the Unionist member of Parliament for Westminster. He was born in America and gave up his father's name (Ashmead-Bartlett) in favour of his wife's, Angela Baroness Burdett-Coutts. Treves and Burdett-Coutts both published books on the war in 1900 (Burdett-Coutts's was *The Sick and Wounded in South Africa: Lest We Forget*; Treves's was *The Tale of a Field Hospital*). The men were set to become implacable enemies, though by a curious irony they shared the same publisher in Newman Flower at Cassells – a shrewder operator than either of them.

The report from Burdett-Coutts which brought him into conflict with Treves was sent from Cape Town on 29 May and published in

The Times on 27 June. He wrote that 'the growing scenes of neglect and inhumanity, of suffering and death, which have been the lot of the British soldier in the closing chapter of this war have made up a picture which it is impossible any longer to conceal from the eyes of the British public' (Burdett-Coutts 1900). In a direct reference to the Reform Club dinner, the disgusted Burdett-Coutts wrote:

> To a mind stocked with scenes which would sicken the hardest heart it comes like a blow between the eyes, leaving one dizzy and bewildered, to learn that at the very moment when these horrors were at their worst and when men were dying like flies for want of adequate attention, a large company of intelligent and well-meaning gentlemen at home, both lay and professional, were feasting on – amongst other things which the war-torn soldier out there would have been equally glad to have – the perfection of the medical and hospital arrangements in this campaign.
>
> (Burdett-Coutts 1900)

Burdett-Coutts also condemned the RAMC for its total lack of preparation for disease in the camps, which could have been prevented by simple sanitary precautions.

The *British Medical Journal* replied rather feebly with the observation that 'The amount of sickness in the forces in South Africa has been large, about 7 per cent . . . but this is less than in previous campaigns'. The journal appealed to its own 'special correspondent' – Treves – for his opinion. Treves decided to answer Burdett-Coutts there rather than in *The Times* because, in his view, this was a matter for the medical profession and therefore no concern of the public's.

> I have read Mr. Burdett-Coutts's letter in *The Times* of to-day, and am shocked and surprised at the report he furnishes.
>
> I left Natal in March, some time after the relief of Ladysmith, and the account I gave on my return to England of the work of the Army Medical Service in Natal was based upon my experience up to the period of my departure.
>
> Mr. Burdett-Coutts comments upon this account as if it dealt with events which were to be in the future rather than with events which have happened in the past.
>
> To every word I have said as to the excellence of the army medical arrangements in Natal I adhere most absolutely.

It is difficult to believe that a department which stood with such credit the exceptional strain of the Natal campaign can have suddenly exhibited the alarming collapse predicted by the writer of the letter in question. My experience had induced me to think that the organisation of the Army Medical Service was sound and good, that the general scheme of work and of administration was efficient, and that the lavish arrangements planned by the Director-General were carried out by his subordinates in a liberal, thorough, and business-like manner.

There was no evidence of the intervention of red tape nor of hindrance by petty formalities, and the hospital work was not only hampered by other departments, but was helped in every way with the heartiest readiness.

I cannot think that our sick have been treated with 'neglect' and 'inhumanity,' as Mr. Burdett-Coutts asserts.

Instead of neglecting their patients the surgeons I met worked with heart and soul, sparing themselves in no particular, and of the untiring and unselfish devotion of the nurses I have already spoken.

This war has been a war of surprises. The casualties have been higher than the gloomiest ever dreamt of, and there was no reason to anticipate that the outbreak of enteric fever would assume the enormous proportions it has assumed.

The circumstances of war unfortunately render an immense amount of suffering and distress absolutely unavoidable, and the difficulties of furnishing adequate supplies from a far-distant base are extreme.

I left South Africa with the impression that nothing more could have been done to mitigate the sufferings of the sick and wounded than had been done when a temperate regard for the circumstances of war was kept in mind.

The Army Medical Service can lay no claim to the gift of prophecy, nor to the power of anticipating the future, but so far as any reasonable foresight can go the department seems to have done all that in fairness could have been expected of it. Mr. Burdett-Coutts will, no doubt, substantiate the points detailed in his report, but his preliminary account is conveyed in language which so savours of the theatrical that it fails to carry with it an overwhelming conviction.

Mobile field hospitals, if they have to do the work they are intended to, cannot take beds with them. It is better for a typhoid patient to lie upon a blanket and waterproof sheet on the ground – as Mr. Burdett-Coutts describes – than to be hurried helter-skelter to the base.

No human being can tell how the progress of an epidemic may proceed, nor how the numbers of sick will be distributed. Preparations may be made for 1,000, and the admissions may not reach 10. It is impossible to avoid overcrowding at times, and equally impossible to provide in every detail for emergencies which no reasonable foresight could anticipate.

That our gallant soldiers should suffer is deplorable indeed, but the blame must fall upon the miserable fortunes of war rather than upon a department which has spared neither men nor money nor care nor devotion in a work which has assumed dimensions out of all proportion to that anticipated at the outset.

The seat of war is at least three weeks distant from the seat of supplies, and in those three weeks a region free from disease may become the seat of a desperate epidemic. The movements of the troops cannot be exactly foretold. It would be better for the country to be flooded with doctors and nurses rather than that the soldiers should suffer, but it is quite impossible that the medical arrangements can at a time of war overthrow all those circumstances of transport and supply upon which the conduct of the campaign depends.

Unfortunately in the war the war comes first, but I should imagine that in no successful campaign has there ever been such solicitous and successful care of the sick.

(Treves 1900)

The letter is a lie from beginning to end, and when the war was over Treves would contradict almost every remark made in it. But while the war continued, Treves saw the silencing of Burdett-Coutts as part of his patriotic duty. At a dinner on 28 June to celebrate his being awarded the freedom of Dorchester, Treves suggested that Burdett-Coutts's allegation verged on treason: 'If this is true, and I am not in a position to say offhand that it is not, it is a statement calculated to throw England into the utmost depths of distress.' Treves's experience in South Africa had made him a hawk. He dismissed critics of the war who 'would like every man to lie on clean sheets, and have a pocket handkerchief and *eau de cologne*'. The next morning *The Times* carried a full account of his speech, and the leading article was highly critical of 'the flippancies in which Mr Treves indulged last night'. For the paper by now had received letters from soldiers who were suffering in Natal, and they confirmed Burdett-Coutts's story.

In order to put this conflict in perspective, it is useful to look at one incident which occurred during the War Office's medical preparations. Sir Walter Foster, the member of Parliament for Ilkeston in Derbyshire, was a distinguished physician and a leading expert on the control of epidemics. He was fully conversant with the usual army medical procedure, and feared that it would not be sufficient to meet the problem of disease in South Africa. On 31 October 1899 he wrote to George Wyndham at the War Department, outlining his views and volunteering his services.

I am sure you will excuse me for troubling you at a busy time, as I have a suggestion to make which seems to me of importance as regards the medical aspects of the South African campaign. I think you have done admirably in sending out Sir Wm. MacCormac [sic], Mr. Treves, and Mr. Makins. They will be splendid from a surgical point of view. There remains, however, the medical and sanitary side. *In all human probability there will be great loss of life from fever and other maladies more or less preventable by careful sanitary work.* To meet this prospect it would be wise to send out a small Sanitary Commission, or a Commissioner with assistants. Such aid would be invaluable to the Army Medical Officers in assisting them to prevent the loss of life to which I have referred. I thought of going out myself for the purpose of lending any aid I could, as I have had, you know, life-long experience as a Physician, and during the last cholera invasion as Secretary to the Local Government Board, I had the main responsibility of the health defence of the kingdom. I fear however that, as a private individual, I could do little or nothing. I therefore write to you to say that, if you decide to do anything in the direction I have indicated, I will gladly place my services at the disposal of the War Office. I am not willing to resign my seat in the House of Commons, and so I should wish to go out in an unpaid capacity.

Nothing could be plainer. The country's leading expert in the area of disease prevention had forecast *great loss of life* from disease in South

Africa. But Wyndham and his colleagues thought they knew better. On 9 November Wyndham turned Foster down:

> I put your scheme of a Sanitary Commission for South Africa before the Secretary of State, and it was carefully considered by the medical authorities here. They think the need of special assistance is not the same in sanitary matters as in surgical operations. The general practice of an army doctor must necessarily make him inferior as an operator to the skilled specialists; but sanitary investigations are among the most important of his daily duties, and he is constantly accumulating experience with regard to them. The Director General therefore does not regard as necessary the establishment of such a commission as you recommend. Lord Lansdowne concurs in this view, and desires me to express to you, when communicating the decision, his sense of the patriotic feeling which inspired your suggestion and your offer of personal service.

Eight months later, Foster had the sad satisfaction of having been right. War Office figures presented to Parliament on 2 July 1900 showed that 133 officers and 4,204 men had died of disease since the beginning of the war. The numbers invalided home due to disease in this period were an astonishing 600 officers and 14,379 men. A further 650 men were invalided home, though the government was unclear as to whether they suffered from disease or wounds or both.

At the end of the war it was revealed that 746 of every 1,000 men admitted to hospital during the war had disease rather than wounds. Dysentery and enteric fever had caused 9,200 deaths.

Six months into the war Burdett-Coutts sent an urgent telegram to Lord Wolseley, who showed it to the war secretary, Lord Lansdowne: 'Cape Town, 1st June. Returned from front, terrible pressure sickness. Breakdown in medical arrangements. Doctors, nurses, equipment, miserably insufficient. Pitiable scenes here entirely falsify statements sent home.' Lansdowne wired back to Wolseley on 4 June: 'Please let me know at once if there is any grounds for these alarming statements.' On 5 June he informed Field Marshal Lord Roberts that 'we are receiving private telegrams of alleged general breakdown in hospitals. . . . A complaint of your hospital at the front has just come in. Is there any foundation for it?'. On 6 June Roberts explained that the Boers had destroyed bridges along 128 miles of railway upon which he depended. He said he was giving the wounded every priority, but that 'a certain amount of suffering is inseparable from the rapid advance of a large army in an enemy's country'. Roberts invoked reports by Treves and MacCormack to refute Burdett-Coutts's allegations.

Burdett-Coutts persisted in sending messages to Lansdowne, who was forced to communicate with Roberts again on 20 June:

> We continue to receive disquieting reports as to state of hospitals. It is alleged that there has been deficiency of medical appliances and comforts, and even necessaries; that there has been much over crowding; that nurses and hospital orderlies are too few; and that proportion of death has consequently been abnormal. We are told that reports made by McCormac [sic] and Treves were optimistic, and that conditions have probably changed for the worse since their visit.

Roberts began to be irritated by Burdett-Coutts, and told Lansdowne that he had heard of no complaints and that the arrangements were the best possible under the circumstances. He did admit that his march from Modder to Bloemfontein was so rapid that his force had carried no tents with them, which meant that 2,000 wounded had to be kept in the open 'until our railway communication with Cape Colony had been restored'.

The Times's campaign, spearheaded by Burdett-Coutts, resulted in a royal commission inquiry chaired by Lord Justice Romer. It began taking evidence on 24 July, and the hundreds of witnesses included soldiers of all ranks, civilian observers like Rudyard Kipling and Sir Arthur Conan Doyle, and medical men. The commission also visited major military hospitals in England and South Africa. In this, the first of two inquiries, Treves and Burdett-Coutts met head on. The report of the inquiry begins with an unusual note from Lord Romer, referring to allegations that Treves and MacCormack had been pressured by the government into giving a false impression of events in South Africa:

> We should add a word or two with regard to a suggestion that has been made, that the civil surgeons employed by the Government were, either by the contract of their engagement or by order or other communication, forbidden to report upon or to state the true condition of matters at the military hospitals. We believe that there is no foundation for this suggestion. It arose

probably from the fact that under the Queen's Regulations all persons while under military discipline are forbidden to publish in or communicate to the Press any information without special authority, or to publicly criticise their superior officers.

Queen Victoria herself was very much against the inquiry. She wrote to the Prime Minister on 5 February:

> The Queen must urge again on Mr. Balfour very strongly the necessity of resisting these unpatriotic and unjust criticisms of our Generals and of the conduct of the War. If the Government are firm and courageous the country will support them. If not, the number of Boer spies will telegraph back to South Africa, and great harm will be done. You must all show a firm front, and not let it for a moment be supposed that we vacillate in the least. An enquiry after the War itself is over can be held, but not now. No doubt the War Office is greatly at fault, but it is the whole system which must be changed, and that cannot be just now.

In its conclusion, the royal commission found that 'The military and medical authorities certainly never anticipated when this war became probable that it would be of the magnitude it has since attained', with the result that 'the Royal Army Medical Corps was wholly insufficient in staff and equipment for such a war, and it was not constituted as to have means provided by which its staff could be very materially enlarged, or its deficiencies promptly made good.'

'It is obvious,' Burdett-Coutts began one of his articles for *The Times* (Burdett-Coutts 1900), 'that for many years the department of healing has not advanced *pari passu* with the department of maiming.' His main contention was that the RAMC failed miserably in South Africa because it was poorly organized. What he sought was 'an improved elasticity in the existing organization to enable it in time of war to take in a far larger supply of civil aid than is sanctioned by its present rules or agreeable to its traditions and prejudices'.

Looking at every aspect of the RAMC's organization, Burdett-Coutts found it lacking. On the medical side, there was no provision for the outbreak of typhoid.

> Hundreds of men to my knowledge were lying in the worst stages of typhoid, with only a blanket and a thin waterproof sheet (not even the latter for many of them) between their aching bodies

and the hard ground, with no milk and hardly any medicines, without beds, stretchers, or mattresses, without pillows, without linen of any kind, without a single nurse amongst them, with only a few ordinary private soldiers to act as 'orderlies', rough and utterly untrained to nursing, and with only three doctors to attend on 350 patients.

(Burdett–Coutts 1900)

He argued that the standard staffing and equipment of an RAMC field hospital was inadequate enough on paper; and that the reality was worse because medical and nursing staff themselves fell ill, and supplies ran out. He reminded the commission that a field hospital consisted of four medical officers, two wardmasters, fourteen trained nursing orderlies and six 'supernumeraries' designed to accommodate 100 patients. On his first visit to a field hospital at Bloemfontein on 9 April, Burdett-Coutts found its staff was halved, and therefore one would expect it to be capable of handling around fifty patients. There were in fact 250 patients, ninety of whom had typhoid. Visiting the same hospital a fortnight later, he found that the staff was still halved and that no new supplies had been sent. The number of patients had risen to 316, and this did not account for all the men who died in the interval. In bell tents designed for six to eight men, ten typhoid cases were packed together with no mattresses or bed linen of any kind: 'the dying against the convalescent, the man in his "crisis" pressed against men hastening to it.' Burdett-Coutts told how

Men lay with their faces covered with flies in black clusters too weak to raise a hand to brush them off, trying in vain to dislodge them by a painful twitching of the features. There was no one to do it for them. . . . At night there were not enough staff to prevent those in the delirious stage from getting up and wandering about the camp half naked in the bitter cold. In one tent, where some slept and others lay with eyes open and staring, a case of 'perforation' was groaning out his life huddled against his neighbour on the ground. Men had not only to see, but often to feel, others die.

(Burdett-Coutts 1900)

Burdett-Coutts singles out for special condemnation the RAMC's failure to provide adequate means of transport for the wounded, who were usually trundled about in ox wagons.

111

With one incident graver than all the rest the dark history of a field hospital at Bloemfontein must close. On the occasion of my last visit the hospital had been mostly emptied, as it was to move on to the front. In the course of this process 20 of the worst cases were removed to a more permanent hospital a mile and a half off. How were they taken? They were lifted out of their tents and put into rough ox-wagons – all typhoids and many of them dangerously ill – and then jolted across the veldt, which in this place is much broken by spruits and gullies. One case was in a state of 'haemorrhage' when removed. The order had come to evacuate the hospital; the medical officer had no choice but to obey; there were no ambulances. In three days four of these 20 men were dead men.

(Burdett-Coutts 1900)

In a speech to the House of Commons on 29 June, Burdett-Coutts stressed that he did not think the army medical officers incompetent. But he did not think there were enough of them, and that the ones the army had were not well enough trained. Properly trained female nursing staff would have relieved much misery. Instead the army used untrained infantrymen who were themselves recovering from illness, and whose convalescence was not aided by the work. But he reserved his strongest criticism for the lack of any system of classification of patients.

There was no attempt at classification. You had men carried or staggering in, one under a disease called 'N.Y.D.' and another under a disease called 'S.C.F.'. 'N.Y.D.' means 'not yet diagnosed'; and 'S.C.F.' means 'simple continuous fever'. These patients were placed on either side of a typhoid patient. I asked what hope or chance had these two men of escaping the deadly disease of the man between them? ... This want of classification was one of the greatest evidences of the want of management that I saw under the Army medical system there.

*   *   *

Treves gave his evidence to the commission on 30 July. He claimed that his Number 4 Field Hospital saw nearly all the sick and wounded of the Natal campaign, and so he was well qualified to comment on the performance of the RAMC, which he claimed 'worked admirably'. But his answers to key questions were equivocal. When asked,

'Did you find you had enough orderlies?' he responded: 'We had enough orderlies for any but too great emergencies – for instance, the battle of Colenso and the battle of Spion Kop. Then, of course, there was an immense rush, and five times the number of orderlies would hardly have met it.' There was also a certain arrogance and (as *The Times* had noted) flippancy in some of Treves's evidence. 'Did you find the quality of the orderlies was good?' he was asked. He replied, 'Well, as far as you could expect work from an orderly, I think it was reasonable . . . as far as the position of the orderly is a possible one I think they did very well.'

Treves was being questioned by Lord Justice Romer. 'So, as far as you are concerned, in that advance [on Ladysmith], you saw nothing that you could suggest wanted improvement?' The reply – 'There are many things that want improvement, of course' – irritated Romer, who retorted, 'I know that, but perhaps you can guess what I mean; was there marked deficiency anywhere?' Treves's reply was contradictory. 'No,' he said; but then went on to add, 'The difficulty, of course, was that of transport. For one month we were twenty-six miles from any railway, and such difficulties as presented themselves came from the question of transport.'

It was the problem of transporting the wounded which had so exercised Burdett-Coutts. Treves took a different view. 'The difficulty of finding any kind of provision for the wounded out in the open made it compulsory that a big hospital should follow the column, and, therefore, we had given us our own transport, which consisted, roughly speaking, of 260 oxen and about 60 mules.' When asked, 'Did that work well?' Treves's answered: 'It worked admirably.'

Romer turned his questioning to the provision of medical equipment. 'How were you off for medical equipment?' 'Very well. The supplies were admirable.' Exasperated, Romer pressed: 'In fact you are not aware of any serious cause of complaint in the course of the campaign?' 'We met with none,' was Treves's reply. As Treves's evidence drew to a close he was asked, 'Did you ever come across any serious case of neglect of any of the sick and wounded?' He answered, 'No, none. I can say that most emphatically. Nobody could have seen more of it during that time, and I cannot imagine a bona-fide basis for real complaint. One has to realise that war is war, and we had enormous difficulties to meet.'

Despite the fact that the inquiry found the RAMC wanting in many respects, Treves continued to take the 'patriotic' line, and published an article on 'The South African Hospitals Commission' in *The Nineteenth Century* in March 1901. He wrote, 'It is satisfactory to find that the graver of the charges made have proved to be either exaggerated or unfounded, and that the medical service of the Army can claim to rise from the ordeal with distinct credit'.

Treves was well rewarded for his service and for his views. His friend King Edward made him a Knight Commander of the Royal Victorian Order on 4 May 1901. He was also awarded the South Africa Medal with three clasps and made a Companion of the Order of Bath. The *British Medical Journal*, ever keen to attach credit to the profession, pronounced that

> Quite apart, however, from his special services in South Africa and his connection with the Court, Sir Frederick Treves had well earned by his ability and industry in the work of clinical research and his eminence as a surgeon any recognition which the Crown could give.

In September 1902 the post-war scandal takes a new twist when Treves is appointed to the rank of honorary colonel in the RAMC (Militia). King Edward was quite aware that the performance of the army in Natal had been less than outstanding, and in August 1901 he said that an inquiry should be held with the purpose of 'searching into the many blunders that were made in South Africa'. When the time came for a second inquiry, however, he changed his mind. In April 1902 the government decided a full public inquiry should be held. On 13 June King Edward tried to persuade Lord Salisbury to abandon the idea:

> The King has received your Cabinet note of yesterday, and he greatly deprecates the conclusions arrived at that a general inquiry into the conduct of the war should be conducted by a Royal Commission. The King saw Lord Salisbury last week and urged him not to assent to such an inquiry which Queen Victoria had also desired should not take place.
>
> The Government is a very strong one with a large Parliamentary majority, why therefore should Ministers pledge themselves to give way to demands from independent M.P.'s? The proposed inquiry will do the Army and also the Country harm in the eyes of the civilised world. No good can come of it,

but it is to be hoped that we may profit by the many mistakes, which have doubtless occurred during the campaign, by a thorough re-organisation of the War Office.... This system of 'washing one's dirty linen in public' the late Queen had a horror of, and the King shares the views of his beloved Mother. Therefore he most earnestly wishes that the Cabinet should endorse them.

Salisbury replied that he could not overrule his cabinet colleagues. He said any attempt to do so might break up the government, and would certainly fuel public suspicion that there was a cover-up over South Africa. However, as Sir Philip Magnus reveals in his life of King Edward VII, Salisbury 'promised that "every effort will be made to render the Inquiry innocuous, and those efforts will probably be successful"' (Magnus 1977).

Realizing the inquiry would go ahead, King Edward gave his support but recommended that Lord Esher should serve on it. He did, and sent the King reports on each day's evidence. The appointment of a chairman was difficult, because whoever accepted the task would almost certainly have the job of writing a conclusion that would condemn senior officials in the War Office. Lord Spencer and Herbert Asquith both declined, and in the end the job was done by the Earl of Elgin and Kincardine.

The 1903 Royal Commission on the War in South Africa was a very different affair from the one held in 1901. Treves gave damning evidence against the RAMC, completely contradicting the evidence he gave to the previous inquiry. King Edward had feared a scandal resulting from the royal commission, but he took two precautions against that. The first was to put his man, Lord Esher, on the commission; the second was to ensure that if criticism were to be made of the RAMC, it should be made by someone whom he could trust: Sir Frederick Treves.

Treves came to the inquiry fully prepared, having circulated a list of his main points and recommendations. The first was that the RAMC had suffered massively from its cumbersome organization. 'It is very elaborately over-organised. It is almost strangled by the mechanical elements introduced into it.... I think the success of the work in Natal depended upon the fact that the military-medical organisation was entirely thrown aside.' Regulations, petty bureaucracy, paperwork and general red tape made it virtually impossible to act in medical emergencies without total disregard of official procedure. Treves continued, 'The length of time taken to obtain the supplies and transport and the like would be such as to paralyse its movement.' The only practical route was to ignore the rules entirely. 'I think I may say with regard to our particular column that they [the rules] were simply suppressed, and the General simply said, "You want so many bearers, get them".' All of these rules, Treves argued, were based on the assumption that army medical staff were incompetent. The RAMC was 'full of an enormous number of safeguards based upon the impression that the officer put in charge of a hospital is likely to be incapable, and that his incapacity will be minimised by restrictions of all sorts'.

Treves argued that the service worked tolerably well in peacetime but was hopelessly inadequate to deal with the uncertainties of war. But even during peacetime, its over-elaborate structure made it costly to run, largely because: 'You can obtain an officer who is supposed to be a specially qualified man who receives high pay, and charge pay, and then he is put to do work which is practically much better done by an ordinary clerk for a pound or so a week.' There was no point in having medical officers if they did not have proper authority. On the battlefield, good medical officers did not bother with the long list of signatures needed to requisition supplies, they simply demanded them. Why not extend this power to them officially? While Treves made some enemies in the RAMC by his harsh criticisms, he was ultimately arguing in favour of the medical officers.

> I would say this, that if a man is good enough to be put in charge of, say, a large mobile field hospital, that man should be regarded as responsible, and should have to a very large extent perfectly free action. As a matter of fact he is not free in any particular. Of course his time of marching, and his route, and so on, must be determined by the General, but the place of pitching the tents, and the question of food, water and other supplies, and his transport, and his general outfit depend upon conditions over which he practically has no control; he becomes a machine, and there is no credit in working the hospital well.

Treves highlighted the absurdity of an incident after the battle of Spion Kop, where of the 715 wounded brought down before dark, all but the most serious had to be turned away from the field hospital because it could not feed them. 'The officer in charge of the hospital was so hampered by the restrictions of the Service that he had no free hand in the matter. . . . There was a large food park close by, and there was no difficulty except in the process of getting in.'

The reality was that senior medical officers spent more time working as junior administrators than as doctors. Treves told the commission:

> In a civil hospital it would be preposterous to suggest that the senior surgeon of the hospital should be answerable for blankets and all those things; that is all done by the house steward, and this particular branch of the Service will never be better until all that work is put in the hands of proper people, namely, a proper quartermaster.

A further absurdity lay in the fact that while the field hospitals were hopelessly short of essential supplies in South Africa, they were over-stocked with masses of useless ones. Treves described the standard issue field hospital as 'theoretically complete' but in reality 'an immense burden'.

> The outfit of the Field Hospital is suitable for any climate in the world, from the Polar regions to the Equator; it is an exceedingly elaborate outfit; it is complete on paper, and that has to be dragged all over the country. . . . I should not be using an exaggeration if I said we could have thrown away quite a half of our outfit and not missed it.

Sensibly, Treves suggested that the problem could be solved by creating advanced medical depots to accompany each column. From them the mobile field hospitals could take whatever supplies were required. Each depot would be run by a quartermaster, and the medical officer of the field hospital would work according to a general rule which said, in effect, 'Take from this advanced medical depot what things you want, and remember you are responsible for the efficiency of that hospital and if you are lacking anything it is entirely your own fault'. Thus, at a stroke, Treves offered medical officers the responsibility commensurate with their rank and pay, and the army a means of accounting for supplies.

Collecting and dressing stations for the wounded were next on Treves's list. In South Africa, the system was for the wounded to be taken from the field to a collecting station, from which they were transported to a dressing station (often at a considerable distance because of the introduction of small calibre bullets with an increased killing range). The wounded were then moved from the dressing station to the field hospital, where major operations could be performed. In practice, Treves said he and his colleagues had the wounded taken directly to the dressing station because 'the men who were put in charge of the collecting stations were either doing nothing, or anyhow that little piece of the arrangement was liable to be disorganised'. While cutting out the dressing station might have some benefits, there were also liabilities. Treves explained to Sir Frederick Darley that at the collecting station the medical officer applied 'a first dressing, which is inside the man's tunic' and tabulated the injury by means of a label. He continued:

> that is really essential, because in one or two instances the label was lost and a man died, and there were no means of finding out who he was as his clothes were all gone. Several men were buried, and nobody could identify them, and, besides, it saves the man from being pulled about twice.

On the question of transport, Treves now fully agreed with Burdett-Coutts. 'The number of lives lost by unsuitable transport and the number of people crippled by it, is inevitably large.' Many of the injuries in South Africa were horrific shrapnel wounds, particularly of the abdomen. But even in the less serious case of a man shot through the thigh,

> if that man could only lie where he was shot he would do very well, but if he has to be lifted into an ambulance and jolted 10 or 12 miles his prospects are very small. There is no doubt whatsoever that the mortality of a war is very largely increased by inefficient transport ... the transport is the weakest thing in the Army Medical Service.

Under questioning by Lord Strathcona and Mount Royal, Treves gave dramatic evidence about the surgical tools supplied by the army. When asked if they 'were not in keeping with the requirements of to-day, and with the advance in the science of surgery and medicine?', Treves answered with smug equivocation, 'Well, it is true, but I do not know whether I should say entirely antiquated. They were certainly antiquated, and we were carrying about with us instruments which I should have thought would only be found in museums.'

The same applied on the medical side:

We took about medicines that were in bottles in the most cumbrous form, and that had been in the bottles for 20 years possibly. It is really a serious complaint; we had to drag this useless chemist's shop all over the country, packed up in the most ludicrous and extravagant way. Tabloids, or any such concentrated preparations as are used now, would have put the whole outfit into a twelfth part of the space.

The stickiest part of Treves's evidence in 1903 was a highlighting of the differences in quality between civilian and army surgeons. At first, the argument focused on the difference in their equipment:

Q. I noted one case given of the inferiority of the surgical instruments used in South Africa. It was asked: 'Q. I suppose civil consultants brought their own instruments with them? A. They did. Q. And there was a very great contrast between the two sets? A. A very great contrast between the two sets. I remember one case on the Modder River of opening the skull, for which one nowadays requires a number of cutting forceps which rapidly divide the bone and enable the operation to be done quickly, accurately, and without shock, but there was nothing but an old-fashioned amputation bone forceps such as was supplied in old-fashioned amputation cases'.
A. That is quite true.
Q. That sort of thing came within your knowledge?
A. Yes.

Since returning from Natal, Treves had served on a committee chaired by the war secretary, St John Brodrick, to consider the reorganization of the RAMC. Its report (1901) contained Treves's proposals which he was now putting before the royal commission. But proposals were one thing and action was another. Treves had visited twenty-two of the English military hospitals with more than 100 beds, and had found that 'they do not come up to the standards of a workhouse infirmary'. Once again, Treves begins his criticism by focusing on equipment rather than the quality of army doctors:

Q. The young surgeons in the hospitals now are accustomed to use the most modern instruments?
A. They are.
Q. And they see operations performed by the ablest men in the profession with the most modern instruments?

119

A. Yes.

Q. These young surgeons, if they go to a Military Hospital, have some antiquated instruments to use there?

A. Undoubtedly.

Q. Can they use them?

A. They have to be used; we had such weapons in South Africa.

Q. Do they not use them at the risk of the patient's life?

A. I do not know whether it would go as far as that. Men have often to do operations with curious instruments. Every one of us took out our own complete outfit.

Q. Yours, of course, was the most modern?

A. I took my own out.

Q. Looking at it from the point of view of having to use these antiquated instruments might cost life or limb, do you not think that it would be better that the most recent instruments should be supplied?

A. Beyond any question of a doubt, if the expense could be met, which I must confess would be enormous; and there are other things almost more pressing, namely, the state of the Military Hospitals in this country. No one could say that there is any Military Hospital in this country which can compare with a large workhouse infirmary, for instance, and that is a fairly low standard of comfort.

Q. Do you not think that is rather discreditable, to say the least of it?

A. It is not creditable to the British Army, I must confess.

Quite apart from the lack of modern equipment, the buildings themselves were inadequate and one hospital didn't even have beds. 'The public,' Treves told Esher, 'would scarcely credit that sick men were kept in casemates; at Chatham sick men are actually kept in old gun casemates.' Field Marshal Sir Henry Norman asked, 'That was not built for a hospital, surely?' Treves retorted, 'It was built as a fort, so that there is no hospital worth speaking of there.' Only eight of the twenty-two military hospitals in England were found to approach civilian standards.

Treves also condemned the sanitary conditions and general environment of the military hospitals.

I had to report upon hospitals in which I myself actually witnessed the washing up of all the plates, dishes, knives and forks in the sink in which the bed-pans were washed out, many of the patients having typhoid fever. It is positively incredible.... As to the temperature of these hospitals, during the cold weather we could not find a ward up to 50 deg., and that is hardly the temperature for a sick man to be living in.

But the real criticism lay in the training and quality of army doctors. Sir Frederick Darley suggested that perhaps this could be improved if civilians were admitted to military hospitals, thereby giving army doctors broader experience. Treves was reluctant to discuss this, and Darley pressed, 'you do not approve of admitting the civilian population to Military Hospitals?'. Treves answered cagily, 'It opens up a series of complicated questions; it practically opens up the question of a state-supported hospital (and we have no such thing in this country) such as they have in Germany and other parts of Europe, and I think the difficulties would be very considerable.' (After Treves's description of the military hospitals one might ask how Darley could even think the public would volunteer to be treated in one.)

The Brodrick committee had recommended that army surgeons be allowed to observe operations in civilian hospitals. Members of the royal commission suggested that if civilian patients could not be brought to the military hospitals, then perhaps army surgeons could operate on them in civilian hospitals. Sir John Jackson asked Treves, 'Is it merely that they will receive instructions through surgeons?' 'Yes,' Treves replied, 'and watch the practice.' 'They could not perform operations?' 'No, that would be impossible.' Treves politely tried to manoeuvre Jackson away from this point by saying that army surgeons should get their practice on army patients. 'Our contention is that if the military surgeon undertakes the surgical work that falls within *his legitimate sphere*, he will have quite enough to keep his hands well in training.' In fact, what Treves was trying to avoid saying was that, in his view (and it was shared by many other medical men), army doctors were second rate, and the only reason they ended up in the army was that no one else would have them. Treves struggled to put his view as politely as possible:

Q. Do you see any particular objection to these Army surgeons having practical surgical experience in the Civil Hospitals for a certain time?
A. Do you mean to take charge of patients?

121

Q. Yes, and to perform surgical operations?
A. I do not think it is possible. I think there would be an immense difficulty in that. You see the hospital has got a certain reputation; the officers are selected with the very greatest care, and it practically comes to this, that when a patient comes in instead of having the operation done by the man who has been specially picked to do it the operation would be done by the first military officer whose turn it was, and I do not think that would be quite keeping faith with the public. I think the public would not like it, and I do not think the hospitals would meet with the support they at present meet if that were done.

Jackson was thwarted, but Sir John Edge took up a different argument. What if army doctors were allowed to have a consultative practice in the towns in which they were stationed? Treves was absolutely firm on this issue: 'I do not think it is possible. I do not think their claim to special knowledge could be such as would cause the public to consult them except in one matter, and that is tropical diseases.'

The simple fact was, civilian doctors had no confidence in their army colleagues – a view put forcefully by one London surgeon to J. Johnstone Abraham, who had qualified in 1901 and was keen to go out to South Africa.

The surgeon nodded gravely when I put the question to him.
'So you want to volunteer, do you?' he said. 'I'd have said "Yes, certainly," to you a year ago when we were in a bad way. But not now. Ladysmith, Kimberley and Mafeking have been relieved. Pretoria's been occupied. Kruger has fled to Europe. Roberts is coming home. The real fighting is over, and Kitchener has been left to clear up the mess. They're putting the Boer women into concentration camps and, if I know anything, that means typhoid. You wouldn't like it. They call people like you "civil surgeons" and make you take any dull medical job that is going in some rotten base camp. You want to be a real surgeon, don't you? The Army is riddled with typhoid – you don't like typhoid, do you? It's killing five times as many men as the Boers. The Medical Service is a disgrace to this country. It's the fault of the War Office. It's always treated its doctors like dirt, and as a consequence it has got the doctors it deserves – a lot of incompetent asses. We do not want any of our good men to go

into the Medical Service. We're going to boycott it until we get proper recognition of our value.'

This was an eye-opener to me. I knew nothing of the struggle that was then going on to get decent recognition, definite rank, disciplinary powers, adequate pay and reasonable opportunities for scientific work in the Medical Services; nor how Treves and others had been fighting an antedeluvian War Office to get these things done, in order to make a career in the recently formed R.A.M.C. more attractive. Looking back on it now it seems impossible there should have been so much opposition to such obvious reforms as were suggested, but there was.

I did not volunteer.

(Abraham 1958)

In the end most of Treves's reforms were put into practice.

* * *

The Boer War started out as just another of Queen Victoria's little wars (to use Byron Farwell's phrase) and turned into an embarrassment and a bloodbath. In one sense it was a matter of national honour, for here was the greatest empire on earth being pushed about by an army of farmers in a remote corner of Africa. As Treves would later admit, there was hardly a family in England who was not somehow affected by the war, and public support was compromised by Burdett-Coutts's reports of the true state of affairs in the RAMC. Tommy Atkins was not being looked after in Natal, and his brother at home could see no advantage in meeting the same fate. Burdett-Coutts's reports were designed, Treves thought, to add to the consternation of hand-wringing mothers, wives and sisters back home.

Treves's decision in 1900 and 1901 was to foresake his independence – and the truth – and side with authority. That he truly believed this to be his patriotic duty may not be doubted. As soon as the war was over, he went on the attack, mounting precisely the same arguments that his enemy Burdett-Coutts had published in 1900. He had proved himself a loyal servant. King Edward appreciated this, and Treves would be rewarded.

Chapter Nine

ROYALTY

Surgery had been exciting. Fame was gratifying. So was wealth. But nothing satisfied Treves more in his professional and social life than the glamour and excitement of his royal appointments. In 1897 he had been made surgeon in ordinary to the Duke of York (later King George V) and in 1900 he had taken the same appointment to Queen Victoria. But Treves's important role at court was as sergeant-surgeon to King Edward VII from 1901.

The relationship with King Edward and Queen Alexandra was more than just a professional one. The King admired excellence wherever he found it, and Treves's brilliance and outspokenness made him stand apart from the gaggle of doctors who cluttered Buckingham Palace and Marlborough House. The King took to Treves right away because he helped him fulfil his role as Prince of Wales – a peculiar state of waiting for a parent's death, in which one is on the threshold of 'power' and always looking for something to 'do'. In King Edward's case it was support for medical research. Treves became not only a trusted adviser, but a friend. Both trust and friendship were cemented forever when Treves successfully operated on the King for appendicitis in 1902.

Treves's relationship with the Prince of Wales took off at a dinner party on 23 April 1900, an occasion on which Treves found himself in competition with a medical colleague before the main course arrived. The competition was the fashionable surgeon Alfred Fripp. Fripp was younger than Treves (he had walked Treves's wards and watched him operate at the London in 1893) and now had a thriving practice which catered to the theatre profession. Fripp had been appointed surgeon in ordinary to the Prince of Wales in 1897 – four years before Treves. He had also been in South Africa, and contributed to the debate on the RAMC. He was miffed that Treves had been the centre of attention in that affair, and meant to draw attention to himself at the Marlborough House dinner party.

Knowing that one criterion for admission to the Prince of Wales's inner circle was story-telling ability, Fripp told a story against the medical profession. It concerned a well-known surgeon and an earl who was ill with stomach cancer in Ireland. The earl was Fripp's patient, but while Fripp was engaged elsewhere the earl asked another London surgeon what his fee would be to come and consult in Ireland. Without discussing the matter with Fripp, the surgeon sent a telegram stating that his fee was 600 guineas and set off without waiting for a reply. The Prince of Wales was 'very indignant'. Treves listened politely, then told a story of his own, which is recounted by Sir Sidney Lee in his biography of King Edward.

> Shortly after the Boer War an English officer, who had been shot through the head, was sent back to England to be trepanned by Sir Frederick Treves. He found that the brain had been most extensively injured and that he would have to remove the greater part. He hardly expected that the patient would recover, but he did, and on leaving the hospital came to the surgeon to thank him. Treves did not conceal his fears that the patient would have difficulties in his profession, since the greater part of his brain had been removed. 'It is very kind of you, Sir Frederick,' replied the officer, 'to take so much interest in my welfare, but thank God my brain is no longer wanted – I have just been transferred to the War Office.'
>
> (Lee 1925)

The King laughed till he cried, and so did Treves in the end. For Lee writes rather sycophantically, 'The King himself, in spite of his wonderful memory, mother wit and gift of expression, was not a good raconteur. But he told at least one good story'. It was Treves's story. Such was the way to win royal favour and the influence that went with it.

Fourteen months later London was preparing for the coronation of King Edward and Queen Alexandra. As Prince of Wales, King Edward had given the monarchy a new image – one that the Queen did not always approve of. He signalled the end of the Victorian era and the beginning of the modern one by dining in subjects' houses, by including commoners in his wide circle of friends and by generally dispelling the funereal gloom that hung over Queen Victoria's reign after the death of Prince Albert. The royal households would have modern toilets and electric lights, and there would be parties and grand balls.

But the role of Prince of Wales had taken its toll on King Edward. He was sixty by the time he ascended to the throne, and he was not in the best of health. He was overweight and suffered from chronic bronchitis caused by the innumerable cigars and cigarettes he smoked. A fortnight before the coronation King Edward was seized with abdominal pain. On 13 June he held a long court but was forced to retire early after a light supper. The next day he felt no better. He consulted his physician, Sir Francis Laking, but insisted on attending a military tattoo at Aldershot despite foul weather. After dinner that night the King's abdomen was distended and he was in severe pain. Laking was summoned again at midnight. He ordered a milk diet and bed rest.

At five a.m. the next day Laking was back at the King's bedside. He had suffered an attack of shivering in the night and his temperature was up. Laking decided to call in Sir Thomas Barlow for a second opinion. They discovered a tenderness in the lower right part of the abdomen. Later the doctors would surmise that the 'chilly fit' marked the moment at which the appendix had burst and suppuration commenced.

By lunchtime the press were demanding an explanation of the King's absence and Laking was obliged to make a statement. He told reporters that the King was suffering an attack of lumbago. When the full story of the King's appendicitis emerged nine days later, the press corps damned Laking for misleading them.

Laking was now treating the King's symptoms with opiates. On the morning of 16 June the King felt strong enough to travel by road to Windsor. Queen Alexandra stayed behind and reviewed 31,000 troops at Aldershot. For a week Laking and Barlow advised rest, a light diet and bed before dinner time. The King was, Sir Philip Magnus remarks, 'a very difficult patient' (Magnus 1977).

Meanwhile preparations for the coronation were going full steam ahead. It was to be one of the grand events in the history of the European monarchy: a coronation to usher in the new century. Every day Victoria Station saw the arrival of yet another royal train, bringing the crowned heads of Europe with their finery, their servants, their fabulous wedding gifts. The King, confined to his bed, admitted to himself in his gloomier moments that his illness might cause the event to be postponed. At one point the pain (both physical and mental) caused the King to remark in despair to Laking, 'If this goes on, I shall give it up. I shall abdicate'.

By now Laking was very worried. The persistence of the King's symptoms suggested he was beyond the physician's reach and a surgeon must be called in. On the 18th he summoned Treves to Windsor by train. The events which followed were wrapped in an air of drama. The King's life was in danger. And there was a need for great secrecy. If the coronation must be postponed, so be it; but not until it was absolutely necessary. Meanwhile, any press leaks about the King's health would fuel speculation which would start his reign under a cloud. So, in addition to the possibility of tragedy, there was an element of farce which largely involved arrangements to deceive 'Post Office officials'. Treves described it to Newman Flower.

> All of us – surgeons, doctors, nurses – were numbered. I was Number 6. Telegrams were unintelligible, therefore, to Post Office officials. In order to confuse the Post Office officials still more, I was always referred to in telegrams as 'Mr Turner'.
>
> As Number 6 I was summoned by telegram to go to Windsor. I went down in an old suit and overcoat, and an ancient tweed cap so as not to be recognised.
>
> (Flower 1950)

The idea of Treves's well-known face with its distinctive walrus moustache escaping recognition simply because he was wearing a tweed cap does not rank among the greatest of his intellectual achievements.

By the time Treves arrived at Windsor 'the local manifestations were well marked. In the right iliac fossa there was an ill-defined, somewhat firm swelling, with distinct tenderness but no very marked pain independently of pressure. The temperature was raised and the diagnosis could be made with ease and certainty'. Appendicitis. Or perityphlitis, as Treves continued to call it in defiance of his American colleagues.

The fact that Laking had summoned Treves meant an operation was contemplated. But an operation on the King was a very grave matter; and an operation before the coronation would have unthinkable consequences. It would take a brave courtier to say to the King that all the crowned heads of Europe must be sent packing, and that all of the arrangements for Westminster Abbey and the crowds that would line the coronation route must be scrapped.

Treves's reaction may be surmised. As an advocate of the interval operation where appendicitis was concerned, it was 'wait and see'. But, at the back of his mind, he was plagued with thoughts of his daughter Hetty. It was only eighteen months since he had made a late diagnosis and then left the operation too late, with fatal results. But the King seemed better on the 18th. Perhaps the attack was over? Between the 19th and the 21st the fever abated. Perhaps the King would get well 'naturally'.

On the 23rd, the King set out from Windsor to London in keeping with the coronation programme. Treves instructed that the King should travel by road so as to avoid unnecessary movement, but to no avail. Ever a stickler for protocol, the King insisted on keeping to the official programme. He travelled by train to Paddington then rode with a cavalry escort to Buckingham Palace. He struggled manfully with his duties, but the press and the crowd noted his obvious signs of illness. In the House of Lords that afternoon, Lord Spencer asked Lord Salisbury about the King's health. The Marquis of Lincolnshire wrote in his diary that evening: 'Everybody took off his hat, except dear old Lord Colville, aged 84, the Queen's Lord Chamberlain, who sat on the "sacks" looking a picture of sorrow.'

Now the real drama began. After consulting with Treves, Laking and Barlow presented their joint verdict to the King: an operation was necessary. And what if I decline? the King asked. The consequences were too horrible to contemplate, came the reply. Laking and Barlow then broke the news that everything was ready for Treves to operate at the palace the next morning. The coronation would have to be postponed. But the King would not hear of it. He must keep faith with his subjects. Laking and Barlow hesitated. Treves reported that the King exclaimed, 'Laking, I will stand no more of this. I am suffering the most awful mental agony that any man can endure. Leave the room at once'. Laking signalled for Barlow to leave the room and 'told the King that obedience in existing circumstances was impossible. Pleading his long service and disinterested devotion, he became as gentle as a woman and extracted King Edward's consent to all that he had proposed'.

For Treves the past week had been one of mounting pressure. The operation on the King – as routine as it had become – was to be the greatest test of his career. Ever present was the memory of Hetty, and the capriciousness of death, which occasionally cocked a snook at the certainties of surgery. On the 23rd he had to make a decision: who would assist at the operation? He telegraphed Lord Knutsford at the London, instructing him to tell the anaesthetist Dr (later Sir) Frederick Hewitt and nurse Haines that they would be wanted next morning at the palace. Absolute secrecy was maintained. Sir John Bland-Sutton later recalled how on the evening of the 23rd he went for a walk with Treves, who seemed lost in thought. It was not until the next day that Bland-Sutton learned the true nature of his friend's pre-occupation.

In the morning the King's three sergeant-surgeons (Lister, Smith and Treves) and his physicians (Laking and Barlow) gathered in the bedchamber. By now a large abscess had formed and was easily felt by the doctors. With the exception of Lord Lister, all felt that the King's life was in danger and that the operation must be performed immediately. Until now, the coronation had not been postponed. Even though the King agreed to the operation the day before, he had hoped there was a slim chance he would be reprieved in the morning. It was not to be so. At ten a.m. the historic bulletin was posted at the gates of Buckingham Palace:

> The King is undergoing a surgical operation. The King is suffering from perityphlitis. His condition on Saturday was so satisfactory that it was hoped that with care His Majesty would be able to go through the Coronation Ceremony. On Monday evening a recrudescence became manifest, rendering a surgical operation necessary today.
> Signed: Lister.
> Thos. Smith.
> Francis Laking.
> Thos. Barlow.

The news reached the House of Commons immediately, where medical MPs commanded the floor with explanations of perityphlitis and appendicitis, what the operation involved, the risk, and the likely period of convalescence.

*   *   *

Before giving an account of the King's operation, the author must insert a rather unusual apology to the reader. When the operation was over, Treves wrote a full account of it. To a biographer, it is probably the most important single document written by his subject. The original is in the Royal Archive at Windsor and a copy is held at the Royal College of Surgeons library in London. Unhappily, the authorities at the Royal Archive refused the author permission to consult this document. However, it has been seen by King Edward's biographer, Sir Philip Magnus, and by Queen Alexandra's biographer, Georgina Battiscombe. Mrs Battiscombe's excellent book refers to it in some detail, and the quotations below are from her transcriptions of Treves's original.

* * *

At 12.20 p.m. the King walked into the room at the palace which nurse Haines had prepared for the operation. The King, uncharacteristically, appeared in his oldest, scruffiest dressing gown, and Queen Alexandra – herself a paragon of sartorial correctness – later told Treves she was ashamed to see him in it. The King lay down on the table as the anaesthetist prepared his equipment. Treves's anxiety was increased by the fact, put bluntly by W. R. Bett, that the King was 'an elderly man, a fat man, and not a good surgical risk'.

From the start, the operation looked like being a disaster. In a letter to the author, Dr W. S. Macdonald of Leeds writes:

> In 1922 I was a House Surgeon in the Victoria Hospital Blackpool where one of the GP Surgeons was Dr W. H. Hodgson who told me he had been associated with Sir Frederick and was present when King Edward VII was operated on for his appendicitis. Hodgson went on to say that there was real difficulty with the anaesthetic so that the somewhat heavily built patient tended to go blue and stopped breathing twice so 'we all had the wind up'.

Treves relates that the King 'at once began to throw his arms about and to grow black in the face'. The Queen, in a panic, struggled to hold him down, and cried, 'why don't you begin?'. As if the anaesthetic problems were not enough to contend with, Treves realized that the Queen intended to stay in the room during the operation. Treves politely wrote, 'I was anxious to prepare for the operation, but did not like to take off my coat, tuck up my sleeves, and put on an apron whilst the Queen was present'. He persuaded the Queen to wait in an adjoining room with her son and two daughters.

At 12.30 Treves began to operate. He made an incision a little above Poupart's ligament on the right side. He had to cut a depth of four and a half inches to find the abscess. He then evacuated the pus and inserted two rubber drainage tubes in the cavity of the abscess. A simple operation. Contrary to contemporary reports and current misinformation, Treves did not remove the King's appendix. The belief that Treves and the King combined to make appendicitis 'fashionable' is ill-founded.

Treves had halted the risk of peritonitis. The pain was relieved. The King's temperature returned to normal almost immediately. When the King awoke, his first words were, 'Where's Georgie [the Prince of Wales]?'. He complained of the sound of hammering outside his window. The carpenters were still erecting the massive stands in the palace grounds which were to seat the guests at the coronation.

When the doctors announced that the King was out of trouble there was jubilation up and down the country. Thanksgiving services were held everywhere, and one preacher began with the words, 'My friends, let us sing together the hymn "Peace, perfect peace". You will find it in the Appendix'.

The King was restless during the afternoon and evening of the 24th, and did not sleep until one a.m. But he was reasonably comfortable the next day, only experiencing pain when the wound was dressed. On the 29th he was able to walk about the room a little and sit on a couch. Treves's anxiety continued for a while as the wound required constant attention. It was important that the abscess cavity should close completely, and from the bottom – otherwise a sinus could appear. Treves was now living at Buckingham Palace so as to keep a constant eye on his patient. But things went well, and by mid-July the King was well enough to embark on a three-week convalescence on the royal yacht the *Victoria and Albert*.

While Treves had been darting about disguised as Mr Turner in an old suit and a tweed cap, his young rival Alfred Fripp was frantically trying to get in on the operation. It is another example of competing medical egos, but a comic tale of hubris rather than a tragic one. It gave Treves a certain ironic satisfaction, because it is a story of 'missing the boat', rather like Treves's early failed rendezvous with Queen Victoria at Cowes. Fripp's biographer Cecil Roberts tells that on Saturday 14 June, Fripp returned to his home in Portland Place after seeing a patient to find Lord Victor Crichton, one of the King's Equerries waiting for him. Crichton handed Fripp a letter from Laking which said: 'Come to the Royal Pavilion, there is a patient about whom I want your opinion.'

(Roberts 1932)

Fripp realized at once that the message referred to the King. He and Crichton dashed to Waterloo, where they were met by a special train.

When they arrived the train had been shunted into a siding. When the driver had got it round to the platform, a telegram arrived for Crichton which said: 'No need for gentleman who is with you to come, patient better, he is to remain in touch, you are to cancel train and return by the next ordinary one.'

(Roberts 1932)

It was signed by Major-General Sir Stanley Clarke, acting master of the King's Household. Fripp later thought that this had been a turning point in his career:

I should not have acted upon the telegram which was not sent by a professional man, and which counter-ordered the request of my professional colleague. I think that in medical ethics I was wrong, and that I should have insisted upon going to Laking, even if I went with Crichton by the ordinary train so as to avoid exciting suspicion. But my long intimate experience of my Royal masters had enabled me to realise how much store would be set upon the secrecy of any possible postponement of the Coronation at such short notice. The King would be thinking of the inconvenience and the loss to others, and I knew Stanley Clarke well, so I rapidly decided to follow the instructions of the telegram, and drove Crichton over to his club in Pall Mall, because there was no train until two o'clock, and went home with very mixed feelings.

(Roberts 1932)

Treves's view was that five doctors at the King's bedside were quite enough. Fripp fretted at home. He stayed in touch with Laking, who assured him that the King was not very ill. On the day of the operation, Fripp and his wife were invited by Lord Esher to view the preparations for the coronation at Westminster Abbey. When they arrived at the door where they were expected, a policeman said that

Lord Esher was waiting for them at the office of works. Crossing Parliament Square, Fripp overheard a policeman say to an American tourist, 'Bless your soul, there won't be any Coronation, the King's being operated on at this moment'. Fripp was livid at receiving the information in this way. He of all people, he thought, should have been first to know. And now the message came to him in the street. His pride was wounded. But the greater injury was to his vanity; and he cast Treves as the villain:

> I subsequently learned that the very evening on which I had
> been put off, Laking had again written a letter sending for me,
> but, altering his mind, he took it back out of the Equerry's hand
> and thought over the situation during another of his endless
> cigarettes. Then he decided to ask a physician to see the King
> with him before calling in a surgeon. So Sir Thomas Barlow was
> sent for and he it was who pointed out that the King had
> appendicitis and from that moment Treves was the greatest
> authority on that disease. Those were very difficult days for me.
> Everybody wondered why I was left out from the bulletins. Sir
> Thomas Smith told me that the King had said to Treves: 'You
> will want somebody to help with this operation,' and Treves had
> replied – 'Sir, you don't want the entire College of Surgeons.'
>
> (Roberts 1932)

Treves, of course, was already the English authority on appendicitis. And, as an advocate of the interval operation, he was conservative in this matter. He had a dislike – not common in all surgeons – of unnecessary operations. Yet Fripp's biographer shows that Treves's vain rival had a clouded and bitter view of these events:

> Following the example of the King in the next few years a
> multitude of loyal appendices inflamed themselves and suffered
> extraction. *God Save the King* chanted a hundred million voices
> across the Empire, but behind the pious wish was the idea that
> Sir Frederick Treves was the *deus ex appendix* in the drama. In
> importance in the public eye he had eclipsed the splendours of
> emperors, kings, sultans, and rajahs. They packed and quietly
> slipped away from the chastened chapel.
>
> (Roberts 1932)

*   *   *

Throughout his convalescence at Buckingham Palace the King was attended by nurses Tarr and Haines from the London. While the King might have been a difficult patient, he was also a kind and thoughtful one. Eight weeks after the operation he appointed nurse Haines matron of the newly opened officers' home at Osborne House. And when the King and Queen visited Ireland in 1903, they invited her parents to meet them at Mallow Station, where King Edward told Mr Haines he had recently visited his daughter at Osborne, where she was happy in her new position.

The King's convalescence put paid to his normal socializing and the Queen spent a great deal of time in his company. Treves remarked that he had to shoo her out of the room when dressing the King's wound. The Queen's 'deafness, however, was a sad handicap; often when she came into the room King Edward would pretend to be asleep rather than exhaust himself by trying to make her hear'.

Finding himself in the position not only of surgeon to the King, but also of occasional go-between to King and Queen, Treves got himself embroiled in a most unusual domestic dispute. Now that the King was recovering, he turned his mind to re-scheduling the coronation. He had settled on August 9, but had not shared this information with the Queen. Unaware of this, Treves mentioned the date casually to her, causing an uncharacteristic outburst. Battiscombe writes:

> By some oversight, this was the first that Queen Alexandra had heard of the matter. Her indignation astonished Treves, who had come to regard her as a paragon of gentleness. The ceremony, she protested, concerned her almost as much as it concerned the King; she was to be crowned too, and she had every right to be consulted. To fix a date whilst King Edward still lay very sick was, she considered, to fly in the face of providence, and she would have them all remember that such matters did not rest in the hands of men but of God. She expressed herself so strongly on the subject that instead of an official announcement of the date, a very cautious bulletin was issued stating that if the King were sufficiently recovered it was hoped that the Coronation would take place some time between 8 August and 12 August.
> (Battiscombe 1969)

The summer of 1903 was one of the most eventful of Treves's life. The King planned to make him a baronet, and this involved a fair amount of paperwork. Since he had to be at the palace twenty-four hours a day, Treves asked his brother William to chase down certain family details for him. The letter of 2 July reveals that since Treves had no son, the title would normally pass to William, and then to William's eldest son. But Frederick had decided that William and his children would not want to be 'burdened' with the title, and announced his decision to declare 'no heir':

> Many thanks for your kind congratulations. I hope you had a pleasant trip. You certainly had fine weather.
>
> I have to prepare certain documents for my Baronetcy and as I have very little leisure I should be greatly obliged if you could supply me with the exact details mentioned at the end of this letter. If you could get me these particulars it would save me a very great deal of time. *The sooner I can get them the better.*
>
> As I must add some place to my title I am taking the title of Sir F. T. of Dorchester.
>
> I am to take a new coat of arms and am having the arms of Dorchester incorporated therewith.
>
> I am told that according to the present form of patent for a Baronetcy my title would come to you on my death and thence to your elder boy. As I imagine that you would not want to be burdened with a baronetcy and as it would be a fearful white elephant to Fred I am declaring 'no heir'.
>
> It will therefore die out with me.
>
> Enid is to be married very quietly tomorrow. Major Delmé Radcliffe's departure was a little delayed and it seemed better that they should be married before he went. They will spend the honeymoon with the father, Colonel Delmé Radcliffe, who has a place at Darmstadt.
>
> Annie and I feel sure that Radcliffe will make her a splendid husband. Annie will I am afraid be cut up at losing Enid but she will be with us some 10 months longer as Major Radcliffe expects to be home by then.
>
> I am living at Buckingham Palace and get away for one hour now and then. Annie has one of the Brighton girls with her to keep her company.

By 1903 the close relationship Frederick enjoyed with William had changed. The tone of the letter is more polite than intimate; and it is clear that William and his family had not been invited to Enid's wedding. Hetty's death had inevitably drawn Treves closer to his only remaining child. She was a beautiful and lively woman who had inherited some of her father's biting wit. Desmond Flower, son of Treves's friend Newman Flower, described her to the author as

> rather tall; but as I was a schoolboy, she probably seemed taller than she was – so I would say medium height anyway. She had lovely blue eyes, apple red cheeks and an outrageous sense of humour. I think that is why I adored her. She didn't talk down to me, but kept me in fits of laughter the whole time.

Enid married Colonel (later Brigadier-General Sir) Charles Delmé-Radcliffe. Born in 1864 – he was much older than Enid – he joined the Connaught Rangers in 1884, living an adventurous army life in India, Malta, Gibraltar and Africa. A loyal servant of empire, Delmé-Radcliffe was Commissioner for the Delimitation of the Anglo-German Boundary when he married Enid; but from 1906–11 he enjoyed the comfortable life of a military attaché in Rome. Enid's life in Uganda and Rome inspired two of Treves's travel books: *Uganda For a Holiday* (1910) and *The Country of 'The Ring and the Book'* (1913).

Shortly after Enid's wedding Treves had to accompany the King and Queen on a three-week cruise on board the royal yacht *Victoria and Albert*. While King Edward's health was improving, he was still not his usual robust self, and he was very sensitive about being seen in public in a weakened condition. When the royal party travelled to Portsmouth by train on 15 July, the King issued detailed instructions to his servants to ensure that he was screened from public view. He was dismayed that he had lost six inches around his waist – a situation which delighted his medical advisers, however.

An account of the royal cruise was kept by Sir Frederick Ponsonby, who was acting private secretary to the King – one of the few members of Queen Victoria's household to be retained by King Edward. Ponsonby recorded his opinion of Treves after sitting next to him at luncheon on the first day of the cruise.

> At the end of the luncheon table there were gold cups and masses of roses. The Queen sat at the end of the table and rang a tinkly bell when the servants were wanted. The Marine band under Lieutenant Miller played soft music outside on the deck. I sat between Princess Maud, later Queen of Norway, and Sir Frederick Treves, the great surgeon, a man with a keen sense of humour but a certain contempt for the human race.
>
> (Ponsonby 1951)

The King gradually regained his robust energy, and Treves allowed him to deal with routine paperwork. But the King was not always in good spirits, and his occasional gloom was not only the result of his brush with death. Despite his immense popularity, King Edward was worried by the spread of republicanism in Europe and the threat this posed to the royal families. Sitting with Treves on the deck one day, King Edward was watching Prince Edward (later King Edward VIII) at play. Pointing to his son, the King told Treves: 'He will be the last King of England.'

Towards the end of the cruise, Treves found himself embroiled in yet another military/medical controversy. Queen Alexandra, accompanied by Treves and Ponsonby, took a steam pinnace ashore to pay a surprise visit to the Netley Hospital. Ponsonby's account of the visit suggests that it was no more than a routine royal engagement:

> The Queen, accompanied by Treves and myself, paid a surprise visit to Netley Hospital. We went in a steam pinnace and, although the doctors and nurses were in the secret, the patients had no idea who she was. She was delighted when she asked one of the men whether he was better and he replied, 'Yes, Miss'. It was, however, unlikely that none of the men should recognize her and soon all those who were able to walk came crowding round, and we had some difficulty in restraining them. One man lying down with his head all bandaged up attracted the Queen's attention and she asked him about South Africa. He replied he had been out at the war for two and a half years and had taken part in almost every big battle. The Queen asked him at what battle he had been wounded and he replied that he had never been wounded at all but that, on arrival at Southampton, he had slipped and fallen down the hatchway!
>
> (Ponsonby 1951)

What the overly discreet Ponsonby neglects to mention is that the visit was more than a mere noble gesture. The King had asked Treves to visit the hospital for the purpose of carrying out a surprise inspection. He also fails to mention that the Queen was much affected by her encounter with wounded soldiers who had returned from South Africa; so much so that she wept openly and unashamedly. Georgina Battiscombe gives a full account of this moving scene:

> Nobody was there to greet the royal party when they scrambled

137

ashore from their launch and made their way across a lawn
where some of the patients were lying on the grass, listening to
the strains of a bagpipe. When the Queen asked one man how he
was getting on, to her immense delight he replied, 'Very well,
Miss.' The sight of so many mutilated and limbless men moved
her intensely. When Treves led up a burly Highlander, blinded
in both eyes, she seized the man's hand and exclaimed, 'Dear
man, I am so sorry, so sorry. How terrible it is! What can I do to
help you?' Touched by her obvious and artless concern the man
burst into tears. Regardless of the onlookers, the enormous
Highlander and the small, elegant Queen stood holding hands
and sobbing aloud like children. She could not be persuaded to
leave him until she had led him back to his seat and done all she
could to make him comfortable. Inside the hospital, as they
toured the wards, Treves noticed the Queen's 'extraordinary
powers of observation'. If the hospital authorities were equally
impressed perhaps they may have been shamed into making
some much-needed improvements.

(Battiscombe 1969)

What the Queen's 'extraordinary powers of perception' had perceived were the appalling physical and medical conditions of one of
the country's premier military hospitals. Treves was enraged by the
failure of the military authorities to implement the reforms which
were meant to emerge from the second Boer War inquiry. On 5
August he wrote a confidential letter to King Edward describing what
he saw. It is the only full account of the primary purpose of the visit.

In obedience to your Majesty's commands I attended Her
Majesty the Queen yesterday on her visit to Netley Hospital.
   The visit was made without notice and Her Majesty was able
to see a number of convalescent patients, to visit the chief
medical and surgical wards and to inspect the operation theatre
and the ambulance train.
   I may be permitted to say, Sir, that the building appears to be
admirably adapted for its purpose and to be well and healthily
situated. From the large amount of ground the Hospital covers I
imagine that there must be difficulties in the administration.
   I do not think that the general state of the wards is, in any
way, as good as it should be and these wards certainly compare
very unfavourably with those of the large civil hospitals.

The rooms are cheerless and the furniture and appliances are unnecessarily crude and rough. The ward furniture was not always as clean as it should be and certain of the bedside cupboards, which were inspected, were distinctly dirty. Speaking generally the surroundings of the patients are comfortless if not actually squalid, and the general equipment of the wards does not approach that of any civil hospital administered on modern lines. I examined one lavatory leading out of a ward. It was neither as clean nor as tidy as it should be nor was it efficiently equipped.

The patients' food – or some part of it – was kept in the wards, was exposed to the air and was certainly not made inviting. On one small bare table were a dish containing fragments of cold fowl, other dishes containing pieces of meat and cold potatoes. Beside these open dishes were two dirty hair brushes and several opened tins. The milk was in pails which were standing in the wards and were in every case uncovered.

There appeared to be a lack of ward kitchens or of means for preparing simple articles of food close to the wards.

I am well aware that a large number of the patients are not seriously ill and that the proportion of cases requiring constant attention is much smaller than is found in a civil hospital; but, making allowance for this, it appeared to me that the general state of the wards was discreditable.

Neither the operating theatre nor the room adjacent to it was up to modern requirements. I was told that there was no appliance for sterilising dressings – I saw none – and I saw no sterilising apparatus in any of the wards.

I do not think, Sir, that blame can attach to the individual medical officers. The system of hospital administration is bad and the present system of nursing is lamentably deficient. These grave defects have been practically admitted and condemned by Mr Brodrick's committee and an elaborate scheme is in the progress of construction which will, I hope and believe, bring the military hospitals to a state of efficiency.

I feel confident also that as soon as Queen Alexandras' [sic] Imperial Nursing Service is established the nursing in these hospitals will be more nearly in accord with modern requirements.

As a surgeon Treves had never encountered difficulty in generating publicity for the issues or causes which exercised him; but after his operation on the King, his fame was such that the smallest remark or activity on his part was judged worthy of coverage by the press. When Fleet Street learned of his secret visit to Netley with the Queen, editors scented scandal. But then as now, editors had political axes to grind. If Ponsonby had been circumspect in his diary, the *Daily Telegraph* went even further in defence of the status quo by falsely stating (on 19 August) that neither the Queen nor Treves had been dissatisfied by what they saw:

> It was stated that Her Majesty and the distinguished surgeon went over the hospital and were not at all satisfied with many of the arrangements there, and further that there was to be a War Office inquiry into the management of the hospital. Needless to say, there is not a word of truth in these allegations, and the hospital authorities characterise the whole story as absolutely false.

The paper did not check the facts with the palace or with Treves. Instead, reporters interviewed the hospital staff, and fabricated a story in flagrant contradiction of the facts:

> On inquiry at the hospital yesterday afternoon it was learnt that what had really happened was this. Queen Alexandra and Sir Frederick Treves paid a private visit to the hospital, and were shown over the building by the principal medical officer. They inspected the whole of the wards and operation rooms, and far from being dissatisfied, expressed their great appreciation of all they had seen and the excellent arrangements made for the comfort of the troops. Queen Alexandra remarked that if possible the high state of efficiency at the hospital was even more marked than before.

But the King, while concerned at Treves's report, had other matters to occupy him. The coronation had now been rescheduled for 9 August – but it was to be a less spectacular affair than originally planned. Not all of the invited guests from Europe and further afield could travel a second time to London. But in other respects the coronation gained in significance. For the occasionally gloomy King Edward, it was a reaffirmation of monarchy against a rising tide of republicanism. For the nation it was a thanksgiving service, celebrating the fact that a popular ruler had been snatched from the jaws of death by a heroic surgeon. Treves was given a special place from which to view the ceremony. When it was over, Treves asked King Edward what aspect of the event had impressed him most. Magnus tells us that the King

> confessed that it had been an incident which 'was not intended to be impressive, and that was the simultaneous movement of the peeresses in putting on their coronets'. King Edward explained that 'their white arms arching over their heads' had suggested, inevitably, 'a scene from a beautiful ballet'.
>
> (Magnus 1977)

With the accession of King Edward to the throne, Treves realized that he had well and truly achieved as much as a surgeon could be expected to. In the year that followed he debated what to do next. In the end, he followed a piece of his own advice given in a casual aside during the appendicitis lecture at Hammersmith Town Hall a few weeks before the royal operation. On that evening Treves discussed a case history of a man who happened to be a doctor. 'Eventually he inherited a fortune, a very large sum of money, and of course the very first thing he did was what any of us would have done – he abandoned the profession and sought opportunity for rest.' While Treves had inherited no fortune, he had earned most of the honours available to surgeons and had worked hard to be, if not wealthy, then very comfortably off. There was little left for him to do in surgery. After a year of contemplation Treves wrote to King Edward on 18 June 1904 seeking approval of his decision to retire from private practice.

> Will Your Royal Highness allow me to state that I am anxious to retire from active practice next month and that I trust Your Royal Highness will approve of my doing so.
>
> I have had 25 years of incessant and exacting work, and of late years I have been almost exclusively concerned with specially dangerous – and therefore anxious – operations. You will, I am sure Sir, understand that this kind of work cannot be pursued indefinitely.
>
> I am continuing to live in my present home in London and shall continue to follow the progress of my profession and I hope that Your Royal Highness will graciously allow me to still hold my appointment as your surgeon in ordinary.

I am most desirous that my best services shall always remain at Your Royal Highness' constant disposal.

Five days later, on 23 June, Treves wrote to his brother William explaining his decision in greater detail. He put his reason for retirement bluntly – he wanted to be 'rid of the business of healing the sick':

Just a line (before it appears in the papers) to say that I am retiring from practice next month, i.e. at the end of the season.

I have been at it for 25 years and have had no easy time and I am now sick of it. I want to go when my practice is at its very highest and not wait until it begins to decline.

I have never done so much in practice as I have done this year. I have had very charming letters from the King and the Prince as to my retirement and I shall keep on – just as at present – my various Royal appointments.

I shall continue to live in this house [6 Wimpole Street] – the lease of which I have just renewed – and shall have my time very full occupied with the Army Medical Service and other public works. I have not the least intention to be idle.

This is the [anniversary of the] eve of the King's operation. I was dining with him last night and he was in wonderful form. There is a very great deal going on. I have to attend a State Dinner at the end of the week and we are all invited to the State Ball at Buckingham Palace on the 8th. I should have gone to Dublin next week to receive an Honorary Degree but I have just operated upon a particular friend of the Queen and cannot leave.

I have had a very decent time but shall not be sorry to get rid of the business of healing the sick.

I hope you are well and that the last trip on the *Moss Rose* was a success.

Treves was only fifty – an unusually early age to retire from medicine. While he had the blessing of the King and the understanding of his brother, the *British Medical Journal* did not welcome the news, and suggested that Treves had an obligation to continue in his profession: 'No one can dispute his right to follow his own inclination in this matter, but his retirement at a comparatively early age, and in the full vigour of health and strength, will be a serious loss to surgery in this country.'

But Treves continued to take an interest in medical affairs, and his influence upon the King's patronage of medicine was considerable. By opening the out-patients' wing of the London Hospital in 1903 the King did much to assist the hospital's fund-raising efforts. He also laid foundation stones at the King Edward Hospital, Windsor; the new King's College Hospital, Denmark Hill; and the Norfolk and Norwich Hospital. In 1897 he had established the Prince of Wales Fund to raise £100,000–150,000 per annum for hospitals. Before his accession the fund only succeeded in raising £50,000 per annum; but after his accession the sum steadily increased, reaching £158,000 in 1910. The fund still exists.

While King Edward was genuinely interested in supporting hospitals and in encouraging medical research, he had a deep dislike of professional arrogance and incompetence, and he found a good deal of it in the medical profession. Upon his accession, the King received a gift of £200,000 from his friend Sir Ernest Cassel to be used for a project of his choice. The King had visited a tuberculosis sanitorium in Cronberg and was convinced that England needed something similar. He explained to another medical friend, Sir Felix Semon, that he wanted an institution which would cater largely to 'the poorer middle classes', with ten out of 100 beds reserved for wealthy patients whose fees would help subsidize costs. The King appointed two committees of three doctors each to put the wheels in motion. The medical committee included three royal physicians: Sir William Broadbent, Sir Francis Laking and Semon. The administrative committee was made up by Sir Richard Douglas Powell, Sir Herman Weber and Dr Charles Theodore Williams. The King's ire was first aroused when the committees (presumably in an effort to avoid doing any practical work themselves) appointed two secretaries at £300 per annum; he was particularly incensed that one of them was Sir William Broadbent's son, John. Then, despite assurances from the vendor that the land was suitable for a hospital, it was discovered that no usable water was available on the site. A reservoir and pumping station had to be built and costs skyrocketed. The whole process took four years, far too long in the King's opinion. When Semon told the King about the water problem, he exclaimed: 'I will tell you something: you doctors are nearly as bad as the lawyers, and God knows that will say a great deal!' As soon as the building was ready, King Edward sacked the committees. He set up a new one to manage the place, and the only doctors he had any faith in were Treves and Laking.

In 1908 Treves went to Paris to visit the Radium Institute. He was excited about the possibilities that radium opened up for surgery and wrote to the King suggesting that an institute similar to the French one should be set up in London. On 23 October 1908 King Edward replied:

> Many thanks for your most interesting letter. Your visit to the Radium Institute in Paris must have been of the greatest value to you. We must indeed endeavour to have one in London, and we can I hope count on the generosity of one individual [Sir Ernest Cassel] you are in communication with, and I know my present host [Lord Iveagh] would gladly also assist. My greatest ambition is not to quit this world until a real cure for cancer has been found, and I feel convinced that radium will be the means of doing so!

The King's interest in a cure for cancer was not entirely without self-interest. In 1906 he had developed an 'ulcer' between his right eye and his nose which was first believed to be malignant. It proved not to be, and was successfully treated by radium in 1907. By January 1909 Treves was able to announce at a press conference that London would have its own radium institute, and that he would be its chairman.

King Edward was generous to his friends, and he never tired of rewarding Treves with honours. After being made a baronet and a Knight Commander of the Victorian Order in 1902, in 1905 he was made a Knight Grand Cross of the Victorian Order. The King also gave him a grace and favour house, Thatched House Lodge in Richmond Park, for life. It was a perfect location for retirement and the writing of travel books. Every year the King and Queen would send the Treveses a haunch of venison, which Treves disliked with a passion. Family legend has it that, instead of offending the King, Treves would bury the venison in the garden. The beauty of a particular yew tree in that garden is said to be the result of this unusual fertilizer. After his operation upon the King, Treves was an annual visitor to Balmoral, where the royal party shot and played cards. It is much to Treves's credit that the King desired his company, given Treves's deep aversion to shooting.

Universities at home and abroad showered him with honorary degrees: Aberdeen, Pennsylvania, St Petersburg. In November 1903 Treves was made rector of the University of Aberdeen for a five-year term. While he had always been a popular teacher at the London he had never stood for laziness or impudence in his students. He knew that Aberdeen had a tradition of heckling rectors' annual speeches, and he warned the authorities that if he heard any voice other than his own he would quit the stage. When he had collected his honorary degree in 1903 the students rose to their feet and sang 'God Save the King'. In 1905 they maintained a respectful silence during his address, then mobbed him afterwards, drawing him through the streets in an open carriage.

*   *   *

But King Edward's reign was not to last long – just under eight years. He had come to the throne at the age of sixty-one, after years of enthusiastic devotion to pleasures which had taken their toll. On 2 May 1910 he returned to Buckingham Palace having caught a chill while visiting Sandringham. He was coughing and wheezing, and his appearance frightened his friends. Laking was summoned, and on 5 May the doctors issued a bulletin saying that the King was suffering from bronchitis and that his condition was grounds for 'some anxiety' – a courtier's way of saying that the King's life was in danger. Despite his illness, the King stubbornly refused to lie in bed. On 6 May he dressed in a frock coat to receive Lord Knollys in the morning. At noon he smoked a large cigar with Sir Ernest Cassel. While taking lunch and playing with two canaries in a cage by an open window in his bedroom, the King collapsed. A series of heart attacks followed. The doctors watched helplessly as he gasped for breath and slipped in and out of consciousness. They gave him morphine. The Queen, their children, and the Archbishop of Canterbury gathered in the next room.

Gallant to the end, the King held court on his deathbed. Many of his friends, hearing of the sudden illness, came to the palace immediately. The Queen ordered that all those who knew the King well should be admitted to his bedroom to say goodbye; she showed graciousness and generosity by including the King's mistress, Alice Keppell. As the King lapsed into coma, the Prince of Wales told him that his horse, Witch of the Air, had won at Kempton by a decisive margin. 'I am very glad', he replied.

At 11.45 on 6 May 1910, the King died. The Prince of Wales, now King George V, wrote in his diary that night: 'I have lost my best friend and the best of fathers. I never had a word with him in my life. I am heartbroken and overwhelmed with grief.'

The last service that Treves performed for his King was to sign his death certificate.

* * *

The passing of King Edward by no means signalled the end of Treves's connection with the court. Like Ponsonby and a few others, he could claim service to three monarchs. In 1910 King George V made Treves his sergeant-surgeon. King George did not merely inherit Treves from his father; their relationship went back to 1897 when King George, as Duke of York, had given Treves his first royal appointment by making him his surgeon in ordinary.

While King George never acquired the same interest his father had in medical patronage, he nevertheless allowed Treves to guide what interest he had. And, as a loyal son of the London Hospital, Treves steered the King towards the East End of the London. In 1898 he escorted the Duke and Duchess of York on the first of three visits to the hospital. The second was in February 1908, when the royal couple attended the Hunterian Oration of Sir Henry Morris, the hospital's president. The third was in 1909, and was the subject of a rather childish conflict between Treves and Morris, with most of the blame attaching to Treves. While Treves was no longer associated with the London in any official capacity, he took a rather proprietorial view of the place. Arthur Keith – no stranger to Treves's temper – was then conservator of the hospital museum. In his autobiography he recounts yet another tale of petty jealousy within the medical profession:

In February last year the Prince and Princess came to Morris's Hunterian oration and said they would like to come back and see the Museum, but in the meantime Treves had stepped in and arranged the visit. He asked our President that it should be kept quite private, only the Conservator to be in attendance; Morris gave a grumbling consent. President handed me a list of specimens which Treves had sent him – particular things which he thought would prove of interest. These specimens were put out in the Council Room. To the list supplied by Treves I added the calculi which our President had removed by operation from the kidney, the first operation of its kind.

Today (March 10, 1909) the President came at 2.30 while I was in the theatre preparing for a lecture at five o'clock. Went with him to look at the specimens in the Council Room and then through the Museum to mark the more attractive exhibits. President, for a big, buccolic John Bull, was jumpy and excited. At 3 o'clock the Royal carriage arrived; Treves stepped out, hat in hand. The Prince and Princess entered and shook hands with the assembled group – the President, Secretary Cowell and Conservator Keith. 'Ah,' said the Prince as we entered Room I, where hundreds of skulls were on exhibition, 'I see you receive us in the skullery!', a joke which he assured us he did not coin. Treves immediately began to demonstrate the dissections to the Princess, Morris to the Prince. The Prince was much interested in the sciatic nerve, as a friend was the victim of sciatica. The Princess caught sight of the case in which the transparent bodies of human foetuses were shown; she became absorbed in them and called to her husband to join her. Treves then showed the skeleton of the notorious Jonathan Wilde, with a coffin plate to prove authenticity. Then came the turn of the giant O'Brien and the little dwarf, Crachami, who stood beside him. The Princess was greatly interested in the dwarf. The giant's skull was taken down and opened to show that he had suffered from an enlargement of the pituitary gland, a condition on which Treves discoursed with practised fluency. On seeing the wax models of dissections in Room II, the Prince at once recognized their identity with the specimens he had seen in Guy's Hospital. Morris wanted to show him a model of the ear but Treves cut the President short by showing a dissection of the nose pointing to the part which a certain surgeon had proposed to remove from his (the Prince's) nose.

'Sydney Holland,' said the Prince, 'tells me there is a great difficulty in getting subjects for dissection; do you have this difficulty?' I said the difficulty arose from the sentiment against dissection which was held by poor-law guardians. He said it was quite wrong that sentiment should rule in such matters. Treves demonstrated the appendix to both visitors and showed cases of appendicitis. The Prince was particularly interested in our collection of the tattooed Maori heads; he knew all about them. Treves said that a Maori head was not the sort of companion to give comfort. Presently we came to dissections of guinea-pigs on

147

which transplants of growing tumours had been grafted. 'Vivisection,' said the Prince, 'has been employed in the making of these preparations; if Stephen Coleridge (the violent anti-vivisector of the time) knew you had them, he would write columns to *The Times* – if it would print what he wrote.' 'There is no other way,' he went on; if Medicine and Surgery were to progress there must be vivisection. The Princess shared in this view. . . . On entering the Council Room, Treves at once set about the particular specimens for which he had asked. The rest of us were in the background, but I kept an eye on the lively demonstrator. I noted that when he came to our President's specimens and read the labels attached he moved on to the next specimen. I went up to Treves and whispered that he had passed a specimen of great interest – the first renal calculi removed by operation – but he went on his way. I saw signs of annoyance creeping over the President's countenance, and, joining the Royal party he sought to amend a description which Treves had just given of an exhibit. Treves went on his way unperturbed. The last specimen he showed was part of the aorta of the Pharaoh of the Exodus. . . . When our Royal visitors had gone, the President, Treves, Cowell, and I sat down to refresh ourselves with tea. The President expressed his regret that his specimens had been overlooked, but Treves merely replied with a little shrug of his shoulders. Morris went on to complain of the vice-presidents and members of the Council being excluded. Just then we were joined by Sir Mayo Robson, one of the vice-presidents. He wanted to know what notice had been given of this Royal visit, but Morris, getting up from his chair, said he could not stay to answer, as a committee awaited him in another room. Before he went Treves thanked me for my help and said the visit had been a great success. So much for one Royal visit.

(Keith 1950)

Treves enjoyed the friendship of the royal family until the end of his life. King George and Queen Mary were regular visitors to the Treveses' home in Richmond Park, and they always included the Treveses on the Balmoral guest list. It was Treves who was chosen to represent the King at the funeral of Lord Lister in 1912, and in 1911 the King had sought Treves's opinion on the medical implications of the Insurance Bill.

While Treves's royal appointments were personally gratifying, they were also significant in the wider context of giving the medical profession, which did not then enjoy the power it does today, a stronger voice in the press and in government. The RAMC was unlikely to have been reformed from within after the Boer War, and a lay surgeon without the implicit backing of the monarch would have had a difficult time steering measures through the War Office. London hospitals, still dependent upon charity for their running costs, benefited from Treves's advocacy of their cause, receiving royal support which encouraged the wealthy circle of royal friends (and aspiring friends) to make generous donations. But the real import of his court connection for Treves was to make him indisputably the most famous surgeon of his day, not only in England, but throughout much of the world.

Chapter Ten

WAR

Treves's talent for controversy found a new outlet in 1905 when it was proposed that he become the first chairman of the executive committee of the British Red Cross Society – which had not yet come into existence. Given that the guidelines for the Red Cross movement worldwide were agreed at the Geneva Conference of 1863, it seems strange to the modern observer that Britain had no Red Cross Society forty-two years later. By 1866 the only significant powers to be without one were Britain, Russia and Holland.

The British Red Cross Society is, of course, a remarkable organization which has brought relief to hundreds of thousands of wounded soldiers and suffering civilians. But the story of how it struggled to come into existence is one of belligerent opposition, bureaucratic pettiness and professional jealousy – things with which Treves was very well acquainted.

In 1870, in response to the Franco-Prussian War, the British Society For Aid to the Sick and Wounded in War was established. Later known as the National Aid Society, the organization was referred to outside Britain as 'La Croix Rouge Anglaise'. Then, in 1877, Sir John Furley helped found the St John Ambulance Association, essentially a peacetime organization. Yet, in time of war, the National Aid Society and the St John Ambulance Association both fell under the umbrella of 'Red Cross' which, after the Geneva Convention of 1864, belongs to a nation's military medical service in wartime.

In 1898 the whole matter became even more confused when the Central British Red Cross Committee was founded. Because it was recognized by the War Office (and members of the War Office served on it), its priority was to aid casualties of wars in which Britain was involved. The National Aid Society, however, had a more generous charter in keeping with the spirit of the Geneva Conference, which declared that

> the aid and assistance of the Society be given in the first instance to the sick and wounded of our own armies, should we unfortunately be engaged in war; but, should the country continue neutral and uninvolved in war, that the aid be given impartially between the sick and wounded of the belligerent armies.

The point of Treves's appointment as chairman of the national executive of a new British Red Cross Society was to bring all of these competing interests together to form one effective organization.

In 1904, while travelling round the world writing his book *The Other Side of the Lantern*, Treves visited Red Cross hospitals in Japan while the Russo-Japanese War was in progress. He was impressed by the international effort, and discounted the criticism that medical and nursing staff from different countries could not work together successfully. Upon his return, King Edward and Queen Alexandra pressed Treves to take on the job of unifying the competing aid agencies. He was uniquely qualified for the job by his surgical reputation, his experience of the RAMC reform both in its professional aspect and in the matter of steering change through the conservative War Office, and his popularity with the public. Treves accepted immediately, knowing that his hand was strengthened against the War Office by the fact that his old friend from the London, Lord Knutsford, was to represent the St John Ambulance Association.

Treves always loved a challenge and he had an admirable record of success. But the reorganization he undertook proved far more frustrating and exhausting than he could have imagined. Knutsford got the ball rolling with a proposal which had the King as patron and the Queen as president. King Edward then appointed Viscount Esher to launch an inquiry into how the proposal could be put into action. Esher was to be assisted by Treves and Sir Edward Ward of the War Office. On 17 July 1905 Treves was able to write to the Earl of Cawdor, First Lord of the Admiralty, outlining the plan. The key item of contention in his proposal was that the new British Red Cross Society was seeking 'not only official recognition, but recognition as the *only* medium through which offers of voluntary aid in time of war would be placed at the disposal of the Admiralty'. While numerous colonial wars had proved the British Army to be lacking in adequate medical provision – largely through poor organization – the military authorities were unwilling to concede that one central body should be responsible for the selection and provision of volunteer aid in time of war. While King Edward had appointed Sir Edward Ward of the War Office to work with Treves under Viscount Esher, the mere fact of throwing the two men together did not automatically resolve their essential differences on the matter. Ward's loyalty was to the War Office; and there were many in it who had bitter memories of Treves's attack on the RAMC three years previously.

At the end of April 1906 Treves was told by Ward that neither the War Office nor the Admiralty was prepared to grant complete control over voluntary personnel. He said the military departments already had arrangements with the Ambulance Department of the Order of St John and the St Andrew's Ambulance Association, and that they would not want to be precluded from accepting assistance from, for example, a colonial government. Treves attempted to get round this by suggesting on 2 May that while all voluntary aid in time of war was to come from the new British Red Cross Society, the military departments would be 'free to enter into direct communication in time of peace' with the two ambulance associations. The War Office and the Admiralty would move only very slightly from their initial position. Ward replied on 14 May that he could not accept Treves's proposal, but would accept an agreement that the new society would be the sole channel for offers of voluntary aid other than those coming from or already arranged with the Ambulance Department of the Order of St John and the St Andrew's Ambulance Association. Treves's committee had to accept. The War Office and the Admiralty would concede no more.

Treves's efforts had resulted in a compromise; but future events would prove it to be a fairly workable one. On 23 May 1906 Treves read a message from the King at Mansion House declaring the objectives of the new society. It was to be responsible for organizing voluntary aid throughout the whole of the British Empire. But first it had to be organized on a county basis in Britain. With the creation of the Territorial Army in 1907, Treves saw an opportunity for local branches of the society to become involved. However, the War Office issued a memorandum which contradicted the agreement with the society as the sole provider of voluntary aid, stating that any organization could assist the Territorials. It was largely due to Treves's efforts that the dispute was resolved through the creation of the

Voluntary Aid Detachments, one of the British Red Cross Society's major contributions at home in its early years.

Treves was also involved in campaigns to recruit more and better trained nurses, both in civilian life and in readiness for war. In an address to the Colonial Nursing Association on 25 May 1911 Treves mustered his best patriotic rhetoric to elevate the nurse to the position of bearer of the torch of civilization to the black masses. The next day *The Times* reported him as saying that

> Hospitals provided the finest education the native received. He was taught to be clean and keep himself healthy, and was shown the sympathy and kindness of the white race. There was nothing so powerful in bringing together the white and black races as the hospital, and in the hospital there was no person so powerful as the nurse. The hospitals had a great political influence in the Colonies. Sir Alfred Sharpe said there could be no better investment for the Colonial Office than the establishment of well-equipped hospitals with good nursing staff in tropical colonies.
>
> (Treves 1911)

*   *   *

But colonial wars were small beer compared with the Great War. While Treves had stepped down as chairman of the executive committee of the British Red Cross Society in 1912, he was back in 1914 as head of the medical personnel department. The supply of such personnel was what Treves had fought for on behalf of the Red Cross; he would be the first to exercise the responsibility.

Before work on such a large scale could start, however, money and premises were needed. The first was taken care of by an appeal in *The Times* signed by Treves, Lord Rothschild and Sir Aurelain Ridsdale which raised more than £100,000. Then the comptroller of His Majesty's Stationery Office, Sir Rowland Bailey, mentioned to Treves that a new HMSO office had just been completed near Waterloo; would that do? It was perfect: five storeys and centrally heated, with War Office contributions it was quickly converted into a 65-ward hospital. There was a concert hall, and Treves's old friend the Duchess of Bedford paid for the construction of a chapel.

While building work was going on Treves set up office at Devonshire House (he later moved to 83 Pall Mall). Apart from assessing the medical competence of volunteers, Treves was looking for people who were sympathetic to the aims of the society and who had sufficient administrative experience to ensure that strategies originating from national headquarters would be efficiently executed abroad. It was hard work, and many of Treves's friends believed that his health suffered because of it.

Treves loved the excitement. He believed that his Boer War experience made him something of an expert in the field, a claim not entirely without justification. Directing the allocation of personnel from his cramped office, Treves encountered many old friends and students. One, the painter Henry Tonks who had left surgery on Treves's advice, ceased to be a friend in that office. During 1915 Tonks was working in a Red Cross hospital at d'Arc-en-Barrois in Haute Marne. He was unhappy there, and applied to Treves for some work to which he was better suited. Tonks complained that Treves kept him 'waiting like a servant' and stormed out. But the account of J. Johnston Abraham – the surgeon who had been persuaded by one of his teachers not to go to the Boer War after Treves's return – shows how effective Treves's management of the personnel office could be, and what an important role it could play in the larger war effort. Abraham was then thirty, and the RAMC turned him down as too old. He was told to go to the Red Cross.

> I did, and I was referred at once to Sir Frederick Treves, from whom I had a very different reception.
>
> 'We're wanting surgeons badly in Belgium, Abraham. Souttar – you know Souttar – is there now. Would you care to go to Antwerp?'
>
> 'Delighted,' I answered.
>
> 'Right. Well, come tomorrow and we'll fix you up.'
>
> Next day he said:
>
> 'Antwerp has fallen, as you know. What about Ostend or Dunkirk?'
>
> 'Anywhere, Sir Frederick.'
>
> Ostend and Dunkirk fell just as it was arranged for me to go over. The Germans were sweeping across the Low Countries. The dream of a war over by Christmas was fading. I saw Treves again.
>
> 'Would you care to go to Serbia?' he said gravely. 'We are fixing up a mission going out in a troopship in a few days. It will

be very rough campaigning, and we can only send men of first-class physique. Could you get ready in five days?'

'Certainly,' I said.

And in five days I was at Southampton on board the troopship, having settled my affairs, got leave of absence from my hospitals, and arranged for a colleague to look after my practice.

(Abraham 1958)

Abraham was in Serbia until March 1915. While he was there a typhus epidemic broke out. He left London weighing twelve stone; he returned weighing eight stone four pounds. He went to Treves immediately upon his return and told him about the epidemic. What happened next may have changed the course of history:

He listened with amazement to my story, for nothing of the epidemic had been allowed to pass the censorship because the Serbs feared they might be invaded if it was known they were so defenceless.

Treves stared at me as I talked. When I had finished he said:

'This is most important. The D.G. (Director General Army Medical Service) must hear of it.'

So I repeated the whole grim story to Sir Alfred Keogh at the War Office. He listened intently, cross-examined me closely and then sent a message which brought a Staff Colonel into the room.

Again I went over the same story to the three quiet men, who sat gazing at me, thin, drawn and weary in my battered Red Cross uniform.

I did not know then that I was repeating my story to Kitchener's Military Secretary. But in 1919, when it was all over, Treves told me that the War Office had almost decided to send an expeditionary force up from Salonika into Serbia, and might have done so if it had not been for the epidemic. But the risk was too great. If they had, it is possible the Bulgars would not have come in on the German side, the Germans then would not have been able to go to the aid of the Turks, Gallipoli would have been unnecessary and the campaigns in Mesopotamia and Palestine radically altered – another example of how disease can change the course of history.

(Abraham 1958)

In mid-December 1914 Treves made an inspection of the Red Cross hospitals at the western front. The Red Cross had supplied 900 motor ambulances and Treves was convinced – with justification – that they had done much to reduce unnecessary fatalities. The quality of equipment and staff had improved a great deal since the Boer War, and Treves expressed himself satisfied that the reforms he sparked had been carried out satisfactorily.

Having absorbed the lessons of the horrific mortality figures from disease in the Boer War, Treves returned to England campaigning for mandatory inoculation of all troops against infectious diseases. On 22 January 1915 he gave a talk at the Royal Society of Arts on the subject, and met with stiff opposition. To put this controversy in its proper perspective, it must be remembered that while inoculation against smallpox was widely practised in Ancient Asia and the Near East, it was only introduced to Britain in the eighteenth century by Mary Wortley Montagu. It was considered a folk custom rather than a medical treatment in Britain until Edward Jenner published a justification of the practice in 1798. However, any suggestion of mandatory inoculation in the nineteenth and early twentieth century met with resistance from groups opposed to state interference with the individual. It became a human rights issue.

After Treves's speech two anti-vivisection groups mounted campaigns against inoculation. The British Union For the Abolition of Vivisection published leaflets in which they accused the War Office of sabotaging their own efforts because the prospect of antityphoid inoculation deterred potential recruits from enlisting. They took out full page advertisements in *Punch*, the *Evening Standard* and the *St James's Gazette* and succeeded in making inoculation a highly topical issue. They were supported by the National Vivisection Society, led by its treasurer, Stephen Coleridge. Coleridge's argument was that 'the liberty of the subject should surely not be violated, even if the evidence in favour of this inoculation were ever so convincing'.

Treves replied in *The Times* on 26 January 1915 with some typhoid statistics from the front:

Of the first 421 cases of typhoid fever in the present campaign among British troops, 305 were in men who were not inoculated. In the 421 cases there have been 35 deaths. Of these deaths 34 were men who had not been inoculated within two years. Only one death occurred among patients who were inoculated, and that man had only been inoculated once.

In view of this evidence, and in view of the grievous injury inflicted upon our gallant troops by those who – in widely disseminated leaflets – advise the soldier against inoculation, one wonders if the Defence of the Realm Act is not sufficiently powerful to put a stop to this heartless crusade and this direct playing into the hands of the enemy.

(Treves 1915)

The rhetoric is identical to Treves's attacks upon William Burdett-Coutts's accurate reporting from the front in South Africa. In both cases he brands a liberal defence of individual rights treason, and calls for imprisonment under the Defence of the Realm Act. Coleridge's reply was that mandatory inoculation was illegal under the Offences Against the Person Act, designed to, among other things, protect the individual against surgical or medical violation. Treves could be a hawkish individual indeed. It is difficult to sympathize with his campaign against the courageous Burdett-Coutts during the Boer War. But the anti-vivisectionists were old professional enemies of medical research, and their agenda was more concerned with stopping the use of animals in medical experiments. The anti-inoculation issue presented an opportunity for publicity. If vaccination serum was not developed through laboratory tests on animals, it is highly unlikely that anti-vivisection groups would have defended the individual soldier on the grounds of 'liberty of the subject'. The arguments contained in the leaflets and advertisements sponsored by the British Union for the Abolition of Vivisection were rather unconvincing on scientific grounds, and would have been even less credible had the public known they were composed by Dr Walter Howden of Gloucester, author of books such as *Premature Burial and How to Avoid It* and *Malta Fever and Goat's Milk*.

In response to the controversy the government did not attempt, at least officially, to make antityphoid inoculation mandatory. Instead it adopted a *de facto* policy of enforcing inoculation by not sending to the front any man who refused, thereby subjecting him to irresistible peer pressure. In addition, those who refused inoculation and remained in England were granted no home leave except in extraordinary circumstances, such as the death of a parent.

The controversy sparked off a series of acrimonious exchanges in the House of Commons, often based on misinformation and wild speculation. Mr (later Sir) Alfred Yeo, Labour MP for Poplar, suggested that there might be some connection between antityphoid inoculation and the presence of meningitis among British troops. After Yeo's third unsuccessful effort to introduce this speculation for debate, the MP for Cork, Maurice Healy, complained that both military and civilian experts had considered the 'insinuation' and found it without substance. Ronald McNeill called the home secretary's attention to any anti-inoculation leaflet which alleged that a member of the Territorial Army had died at Lytham as a result of inoculation, and that his death certificate had falsely given another cause of death.

The inoculation issue took another turn when Treves visited Red Cross facilities in Malta, Egypt and the Dardanelles from 1 May until 15 June 1915. Soon after his return Treves fell seriously ill, and Buckingham Palace took the unusual step of issuing a bulletin stating that he was ill and confined to his bed at Thatched House Lodge in Richmond Park, though his condition was improving. Treves believed his illness – it is impossible to diagnose what it was – was caused by infection from flies, and said as much in an address on hygiene read in his absence by Bishop Boyd Carpenter. Buckingham Palace had issued a notice on Treves's condition because anti-inoculationists scented a major propaganda opportunity. If Treves had been inoculated against typhoid and fallen ill with it, then he was living proof that the measure was unreliable. And if he had fallen ill because he had refused to be inoculated, then he was guilty of bad faith. On 14 July William Thorne, Labour MP for West Ham,

> asked the Under-Secretary of State for War whether he was aware that Sir Frederick Treves had acquired a complaint in Alexandria which had got gradually worse; whether he would state the nature of the complaint; whether Sir Frederick had been inoculated with any vaccine or serum previous to its occurrence; and whether he would state with what vaccine or serum or other such preparation he was inoculated.

The under-secretary, Harold Tennant, replied: 'I have no information on this matter, and if I had I doubt whether I should be justified in making it public.' He was greeted with cries of 'Hear! Hear!'. Given the well-known typhoid statistics from the Boer War and the convincing ones in favour of inoculation that Treves himself published in *The Times*, it is unlikely that Treves would have travelled to the front – either in the Dardanelles or in France, for that matter – without taking the precaution of inoculation. Treves was capable of bad faith, as he was in his treatment of Burdett-Coutts during the Boer War. But this was not a matter of ethics or 'patriotism': it was a simple and pragmatic matter of life and death. Treves was nothing if not a pragmatist; and he was better acquainted with death than most.

The most enduring monument to Treves's work during the Great War is the Star and Garter Home in Richmond, established to provide a home for the incurables and disabled of the present and subsequent wars. It was conceived by Treves as a dignified refuge for those whose amputations, paralysis or other incurable conditions would deny them long-term care in civilian hospitals.

The site chosen was that of the former Star and Garter Hotel, erected in 1738, and it was Queen Mary's wish that the name be retained. The £50,000 required to build the hospital was raised by the Women's Hospital Fund and by the profits from a book Treves compiled with George Goodchild, *Made in the Trenches* (1916) – an anthology of poems, drawings and miscellaneous writings by and for soldiers. Sir Giles Gilbert Scott, architect of Liverpool's Anglican Cathedral and Waterloo Bridge, gave his services gratis. When the Star and Garter Home opened it offered beds for 300 incurable veterans of the Great War. The hospital had many more applications than beds; but Treves conceived and executed in a short span of time an admirable contribution to relieving the misery of those who had served their country and paid a high price for it.

After the war it was announced in the King's birthday honours list of 1918 that Treves was to be awarded the Companion of Honour – the lowest rank of certain orders of knighthood. Treves refused the honour – an almost unimaginable thing to do at that time. *The Times* pointed out on 27 June that Treves's refusal could not have been based upon 'any dislike of title as such . . . the presumption is that there has been a mere misunderstanding about the value of the offer.' Treves had already received honours of much higher value from King Edward. But he had remained on extremely cordial terms with King George and Queen Mary. There seems to be no definite answer to the question of why King George offered such a lowly honour to Treves or why Treves refused it. One answer may be that he had been expecting elevation to the House of Lords in recognition of his contributions to surgery and public life.

Whether or not that speculation is justified, an event of the following year shows Treves's character in its most favourable light. Bertrand Dawson – one of Treves's physician colleagues in the royal household, and the man who assisted King George VI's euthanasia – had been appointed physician extraordinary to King Edward largely on Treves's recommendation. Dawson's biographer Francis Watson tells us that King Edward left the final selection to Treves and his wife. They were to entertain the Dawsons at their house in Richmond Park and report back. In fact it was Dawson's wife Ethel who was under scrutiny rather than Dawson himself, whose medical skills were well proven. Not long after the dinner

> Treves sent for them both to Eastbourne, where he was staying at a hotel. At the end of the visit he took Ethel aside and said with a smile: 'Yes, I certainly think you'll do.' 'So he told you', said Bertie to Ethel on their way back to London. 'Told me what?' 'That he is recommending me to the King.' The social as well as medical qualifications had been found satisfactory. Bertrand Dawson was appointed Physician-Extraordinary to King Edward VII.
>
> (Watson 1950)

Treves made much of Dawson's helpfulness and tact after the death of King Edward, and it was Dawson who treated the King after a serious injury from a horse while touring the western front in 1915.

At the end of 1919 Dawson was made Lord Dawson of Penn after his committee report on medical and allied services, which did much to shape modern health care in Britain. It was a notable achievement, but it may be doubted whether his contribution to medicine or to public life was as great as Treves's. If Treves had turned down the Companion of Honour in protest against not being made a peer, he showed admirable generosity of character in his letter of congratulations to Dawson. Everything in it applies to Treves himself, and without taking away anything from Dawson's honour, it serves as a fitting epitaph to Treves's distinguished career as a surgeon to the kings and queens of England:

> I have just seen the astounding and gratifying announcement in *The Times* [Treves had retired to Monte Carlo] and hasten to send you my hearty congratulations. It is an occasion, however,

for something more than mere congratulations or for reiteration of the undoubted fact that the honour is well deserved. It is, above all things, a very great achievement not only for you personally but for the whole medical profession. Medicine, until now, has been practically unrepresented in the councils of this country. The voice in the Commons has been so feeble as to be almost inaudible, while in the Lords Lister did nothing and Ilkeston less than nothing.

You have the ball at your feet. More will be expected of you than any one man can possibly accomplish, but don't be discouraged.

The whole profession will be delighted. The only men who will be jealous will be the little men who count for nothing. The London will be distended with justifiable pride.

Chapter Eleven

ADVENTURE

At the age of fifty Treves wanted to be 'rid of the business of healing the sick'. But there was a more positive reason for wanting to retire. Behind his formidable reputation and sometimes distancing wit, Treves had the imagination of a boy. A corner of his mind was always reserved for the idea of adventure: pirates, intrigue, distant lands, strange customs. His career had not been without adventure. It is a truism to say that the Great War did much to create the notion of travel and tourism, but it is certainly the case that Treves's experience of South Africa and the European battlefields had instilled in him an unquenchable *wanderlust*. Treves's plan was to travel, and to make travel both work and pleasure. Despite his retirement, Treves could not let go of the urge to work, and travel writing combined pleasure, work and profit in a unique way.

The teaching of William Barnes, and his friendship with Thomas Hardy, had stimulated in Treves a lifelong interest in literature. And while he had yet to turn his hand to *belles lettres*, many of his medical writings proved that he had a fluid, accessible style marked by clarity and wit. Treves's decision to write travel books was encouraged by Newman Flower of Cassell. All that remained was to choose a destination.

Never one to do things by halves, Treves decided on a round the world voyage. His subject would be everywhere, a king of utopia in reverse. And, at that time, everywhere was more or less the British Empire. Treves, despite his uniqueness of character, was quintessentially a man of his place and time. He was English and believed in England and her empire; and he was a surgeon who believed that English surgery was correct surgery. What made him unusual as a travel writer, however, was what might be called his microscopic sense of the larger environment. His early life had been spent in anatomical research and teaching, and the practical application of that knowledge to surgery: that is the essence of his scientific achievement. For Treves, anatomy was more than just a job; it was a world view. The human body was a territory. It had a disarmingly accessible exterior and a mysterious, inaccessible interior. His ambition had been to penetrate the body and find what lurked in that dark interior. The job was one of exploration. The result was an accurate map which would guide those whose business it was to work in the dark interior.

Treves's approach to travel is directly analogous. He accepted the outer face of a country as more or less self-evident; but his real concern was to penetrate to the interior, and to find the country revealed by places, things, individuals, minutiae. Empire was directly analogous to surgery for Treves. The surgeon's task was to enter the dark place and restore order where chaos reigned. The job of the colonizer was to penetrate the dark interior and impose British order – law, administration, religion, commerce – upon an assumed disorder, or absence of order. The fact that other, less laudable motives were involved did not exercise Treves much. But the result of this analogous view was a series of books which, at their best, are unique in their powerful observations of a world now lost forever.

Treves always travelled with his wife; and on this first voyage (in 1904) they were accompanied by their daughter Enid, whose husband was busy delimiting the Anglo-German border in Uganda. King Edward heartily approved Treves's plan, and arranged for him to stay with the Viceroy of India, Lord Curzon. The Treveses arrived in December, and Lord Curzon wrote to King Edward in anticipation of their visit, giving the news that Treves's presence had already caused a stir on the sub-continent:

> The Viceroy will gladly give any facilities in his power to Sir
> Frederick Treves and hopes to entertain him and Lady Treves at
> Calcutta. His arrival in India was most opportune, for he went
> up to Simla at once to see Lord Kitchener's leg, about which the
> local surgeons were it is believed about to make some mistake.
> As it is Kitchener will now be down in Calcutta before
> Christmas which will be a reasonably rapid recovery.

Five weeks later, Curzon reported to Lord Knollys: 'Sir Frederick Treves turned up the other day on the way through to Burma. A most charming and cultivated man. I gave him his letters and sent him on his way rejoicing. On January 28 he returns and the entire family come to stay with me here for a few days.'

But these letters give a false impression of what *The Other Side of the Lantern: An Account of a Commonplace Tour Round the World* (1905) would be like. Treves sought the everyday, the commonplace. It was an uncertain and sometimes dangerous search, but the English book-buying public loved it. The first printing of *The Other Side of the Lantern* sold out in a week and was reprinted five times in four months. It stayed in print for twenty-eight years, a remarkable achievement for a book of its kind.

Treves's method was to begin at the beginning, and to establish a confidential tone with his reader. In his assessment of what might appeal to the popular mind, Treves often chose a slightly sentimental tone (a defence mechanism learned from years of presiding over death) occasionally tinged with harsh judgements. Typical of the manner is the introductory chapter of his first travel book, 'The Starting From Tilbury'. The journey has yet to begin, but Treves has already started writing:

> Half crouching behind a pile of rusty boiler plates one solitary
> sobbing woman is trying to hide herself and yet keep her eyes on
> the ship. She is the only one of the 'friends' who has deliberately
> failed to catch the special train. She alone of the host has
> remained to see the vessel start on its way. She is a middle-aged
> widow of lamentable aspect, who has come to see her only son
> off to India. As she watches, she mops her eyes with a
> handkerchief rolled up into an anguished ball. She hides because
> her dear son would be vexed if she had not returned by the train
> as he had ordered her. The dear son at the moment is drinking
> whiskey and water in the second class saloon with unrestrained
> delight. He has already confided to an acquaintance of an hour
> how much money 'he has screwed out of the old mater'.
> It is the 'old mater' alone who watches the ship glide away
> and be lost in the mist.
>
> (Treves 1905)

There is something distinctly modern (rather than Victorian) in Treves's attention to detail and his method of keeping his eye on two scenes at once, one outside and one inside the ship. What also marks Treves as a cryptomodern is his preoccupation with the theme of time, the domain of Proust, Woolf, and others with whom he might be thought to share very little. In his description of the 450 pagodas of Malay (there are actually 730, he points out), he finds the endless sameness of the monuments, row upon row, 'appalling'; but he finds a clue to their purpose in his conclusion that

> This drear picture of monotony, this dismal realisation of unvariableness is as numbing as an ever-repeated 'no', or as a chant droned over a thousand times. If the shut-in court were to reach for miles, and if a man were to lose his way among these interminable dumb lanes, he would have forced upon him some conception of eternity before he gained the outer air.
>
> (Treves 1905)

In the landscape south of Delhi he finds an inexorable sense of timelessness which has no respect for persons; but in observing the labour of plank carriers in the hills of Simla, Treves understands in human terms the monotony of poverty, of relentless toil, of undifferentiated existence.

> I met the men with the planks. They are hillmen of the poorer sort who carry planks of sawn wood into Simla. Each beam is from twelve to fourteen feet in length, and two to three make up a load. The men are ill clad, and the sun and rain have tanned them and their rags to the colour of brown earth. They bear the planks across their bent backs, and the burden is grievous. They come from a place some days journey towards the snows. They plod along from the dawn to the twilight. They seem crushed down by the weight of the beams, and their gait is more the gait of a stumbling beast than the walk of a man. They move slowly. Their long black hair is white with dust as it hangs by each side of their bowed down faces. The sweat among the wrinkles on their brows is hardened into lamentable clay. They walk in single file, and when the path is narrow they needs must move sideways. . . . No funeral procession of silent, hooded figures could be more horrible than this. The path is in a solitude among bare and pitiless hills; the road is as old as the world, and in the weary dust of it many hundreds have dropped and died.
>
> There along it steals this patient line of groaning men, bending under the burden of the planks upon their backs. Behind them a rose-tinted light is falling upon the spotless

snows, and it needs only the pointing figure of Dante, on one of the barren peaks, to complete the picture of a circle in Purgatory.

(Treves 1905)

So too does the Ganges represent time: the immediacy of it as a receptacle for the sewage of Benares, its link with eternity through religious bathing rites, and stark reminders of mortality as pieces of half-cremated corpses float past.

Treves's conception of topography has three elements. One is the land, people and customs of the colonial map, while another is the map of the ever-changing battlefield and the institutions of law, administration, religion and commerce. But the most interesting part is the dark, internal landscape of the mind; not necessarily the mind of the individual found in foreign parts, to which Treves had limited access, but Treves's own mind, and his ability to translate his own fears and anxieties onto the page. Much of the writing has a night-mare quality, such as this description of a mangrove swamp near Singapore:

> In the undergrowth of this swamp of despair are horrible fungi, bloated and sodden. Some are scarlet, some are spotted like snakes, some have the pallor of a corpse. All seem swollen with venom. There are ghastly weeds, too, lank, colourless, and sapless – the seedlings of a devil's garden. Their sickly petals point skywards in a kind of hopeless mockery. Out of the slime come crawling things, and among them loathsome land crabs whose legs scratch among the black pulp of rotten leaves ... one might fancy a hunted man in its most putrid hollow brushing the vermin from his wet rags and listening with terror to the tramp of eager feet about the margin of the mire.

(Treves 1905)

One suspects that Treves himself is the *hunted* man in the nightmare-like passage which imbues innocent vegetation with overwhelming menace; he is certainly the *haunted* man in this account of Canton as a nightmare come to life, in which the people are murderous devils:

> Canton is a nightmare city, and it is hard to conceive of a more ghastly dream than to be lost in its maze of cruel streets. Everything is strange, the dark ways are cramped and sinister, and shut in from the sky. They seem to lead on for miles and

miles, so that one might wander for days before the outer wall and the green fields are reached. The streets are like corridors in a prison, like subterranean trenches, like cuttings in a mine. The high walls on either side seem to be creeping together. There is a fear that the causeway will become narrower and narrower, until at last the wayfarer must be crushed between the greasy stones. The stench in the air is unbreathable as a gas. The alleys are full of a sallow crowd, some in dingy clothes, some with bare yellow skins. They have shaven heads and grinning teeth. As the terror-stricken man in the dream hurries by like a hunted thing from lane to lane, they all stare with curious faces. There comes to him a memory of the devilry of the people, of their murderous risings, of their fiendish cruelty.

He is filled with piteous alarm. He is imprisoned. He is seized with a frenzy to escape before the painted walls close in, before the fumes of the place stifle him, or the growing crowd trample him into the mud. There is no sound about the place like the sound of cities, only a muttering in an unknown tongue, and the slimy tramp of thousands of bare feet. More terrible than all, the panting man in the dream is utterly alone.

(Treves 1905)

While Treves was, as much as any English writer of the time, imbued with a sense of the superiority of his race and its consequent assumption of the inferiority of other races, this prose goes beyond 'racism' to assume an incandescent quality of unconscious fear: the ultimate seed of self-destruction within the colonizer's heart. On the one hand the passage may have been inspired by an incident the Treveses witnessed upon arriving in Canton:

a man had been strangled to death on the quay by the upholders of the law for a robbery committed on a steamer. He was brought to die at the scene of his crime. Those who landed at Canton for the first time on the day of this event must be haunted by this 'street scene' in the nightmare city. The man is suspended in a pyramidal framework of wood. On the summit of this is a horizontal board with a hole in it, just large enough to take his neck. His toes barely touch the ground, as he hangs by his head. Death comes slowly to those who find themselves in this fiendish trap. They may live a day or more, I was told.

(Treves 1905)

But the simple explanation that Treves's Canton nightmare was caused by this event is contradicted by his assumption that the Chinese character contains, no matter how friendly the individual might appear, the capacity for unspeakable evil:

> The Chinese are by nature kindly, affectionate, and docile, yet when the firebrand of riot glares over the city, they are yelling, maniacal demons, monsters of murder, arson, and rapine. I have watched, in a garden in Burmah, a Chinaman who was nurse to a little fractious English girl. That he was trusted absolutely was evident, while his gentleness, his patience, his much tried forbearance were wonderful to see. Yet take this very man back to the slums of Canton whence he came, strip him, and turn him into a coolie again, touch some spot on his brain with a spark that is just aglow in the town, and he changes into a devil, venomous with treachery, and fevered with the most fiendish cruelty.
>
> (Treves 1905)

While Treves had an irrational fear of the Chinese, he was enchanted by the Japanese. One of the fascinating qualities of Treves's travel books is that he wrote them as he travelled, and first impressions are frequently revised. When he first arrived in Japan Treves was disappointed. His expectations were 'based upon fans and screens and the literature of romance', and these were not immediately satisfied. However, as the weeks passed, Treves began to penetrate the formality of Japanese manners and to discover the only culture he ever believed could rival that of the British. He admired the order of Japan, its careful austerity in design, its delicately conceived gardens, its art and the richness of everyday life. The best example that he could find to explain his view to the common reader was an account of an expedition to buy an incense burner. Choosing shopping as his theme, he wrote: 'There are many in the Western world who devote much time and ingenuity to this butterfly-like pursuit; but it is only in the East that the art and science of shopping has reached heights which may be considered great or satisfying.' Few writers of the time paid such close attention to an activity presumed so common; yet, for Treves, the experience is a key to Japanese culture:

Wishing to buy an incense burner, I took counsel with a Japanese friend on the matter. He knew a potter who made such things, but he added that the potter in question was also a poet of some note, and that the business would occupy an afternoon. It did. We went in rickshaws to the outskirts of the town, where we stopped in front of a rustic gate. The gate opened into a garden, about eight feet wide, which ran between the house and an enclosing palisade of bamboo. The house was approached by stepping stones which crossed a strait of raked earth intended to represent a rushing trout stream.

The garden showed a sweep of green, undulating downs, with storm-blown pine trees here and there, a thicket of shrubs, and some lichen-covered boulders from a moor. Although this stretch of country was but fifteen feet in length it was easy to fancy that it would be a Sabbath day's journey to tramp from one end of the downs to the other against a March wind.

In England the backyard of a potter's house would present a water butt, a perambulator, and a ruinous dog kennel, together with a dust bin, some packing cases, and a pile of empty bottles. Any attempt at landscape gardening would end at a circular flower bed circumscribed by tiles.

A verandah looked into the potter's garden, and here we removed our shoes, and entered the house. The poet received us. He was a solemn man, who looked more like a poet in his long sleeved kimono than he would have done had he adopted the orthodox velvet jacket, the loose flying necktie, and the flopping hair of the West.

The room we came into was purely Japanese. It was disfigured by neither tables nor chairs, so we sat on the floor. On the mats was a bronze charcoal stove and a low, black lacquer table, upon which was served, in due course, tea and cakes. The prevailing colours of the room were French grey and maize-yellow. The simplicity of it was relieved by small cupboards with sliding panels on which flowers were painted upon a background of dull gold, by a kakemono in black and cardinal red upon the wall, and by exquisite rammas or friezes of carved woodwork between the ceiling and the wall. The semi-transparent screens which divided this room from the next were furnished with sunken 'finger plates' in dark bronze. The ceiling was of seaweed-brown wood – cryptomeria in tiny beams – relieved by yellow rods of untouched bamboo. Paint or varnish in this dignified chamber would have been as out of place as a wall-paper or a firestove ornament.

The Japanese room is a room in outline, a sketch in water colours, a few masterly lines drawn to make a setting for the blue vase of azalea which forms the centre of the little salon.

After a most leisurely tea drinking the potter poet opened an old gilded box, and taking out a piece of incense put it in a bronze burner, which was older still. The smoke, as it rose, he gathered up in his hands and carried to his nose, and he invited us to do the same. Then out of various cupboards he began to take treasures – one by one – and absently he placed them on the floor beside us. During this stage in the ceremony of shopping it was his pleasure that we smoked. In due course he sat down again and smoked also, the while he handled the pieces of china with evident affection. Among them, however, there was no incense burner.

We then went through the kitchen of the house – where was a small shrine to the Fox Goddess Inari – to see the potter's shed at the back of the building. After watching two leisurely men at work for a while we returned to the grey and yellow room, and ate sweet cakes with ostentatious disregard of time.

Finally from the cupboard was produced – as an after thought – an incense burner. It was a little pot of mushroom coloured china, on which was wrought a pearl grey dragon moving through white clouds. The cap was of the plainest iron. The whole was the product of the potter's own imagining, and both the pot and the iron cover were the work of his hands.

There then came some dreamy talk about yen, which talk was dropped on occasion and then incontinently resumed. Finally, and by unconscious steps, the incense burner, with its pearl grey dragon, passed into my possession. When the rickshaws finally took us back to the town the day was far spent.

(Treves 1905)

Treves's well developed aesthetic sense and his tentative modernity enabled him to appreciate Japanese lightness and austerity as con-trasted with British Victorian clutter. But one of the more surprising clues to his character comes from his observations on the Shinto religion. Treves was brought up in a God-fearing household and retained enough practical Christianity in his adult life to read the Bible to Joseph Merrick and to work for the Mission to Deep Sea Fisherman and the Boys' Brigade. Tolerance of 'foreign' religions was not a hallmark of the British colonizing enterprise, but the simplicity of the Shinto faith held a strong appeal for Treves:

> It is the simplest of all the faiths of the world. Shinto merely means 'God's way,' and to the founders of the sect 'God's way' must have been a way of pleasantness and a path of peace. Shintoism possesses neither sacred books nor an austere code of ethics. It has burdened itself with no dogmas, while the unseemly cackle of theological discussion has never come within its tree-encircled walls. Of the malignity of religious hate, of the bitterness of religious persecution, the Shinto faith knows nothing.
>
> It has been to the people the familiar friend, not the pedagogue; the comforter, not the censor.
>
> (Treves 1905)

These gentle observations open a window on Treves's character, usually perceived by his contemporaries as aggressive (even ruthless), ambitious, sarcastic, dismissive and somewhat vain, though brilliant. Do we detect the faintest longing for something other than the orthodoxy to which he had subscribed since a child? For a collective individuality rather than national acceptance of dogma? For a society in which pacifism might rule? For a minimum of interference in individual life by authority? Perhaps. But while Treves marvelled at the difference between Shintoism and Christianity, he also found similarities between Shintoism and some English values he admired, especially patriotism and duty. But he stubbornly admired the *difference* between Shintoism and Christianity, particularly the fact that in the former, moral values derived not from belief in a remote deity, but from a sense of obligation which attached to the memory of the dead:

> Ancestor worship has made it the religion of the state as well as the religion of the family. With that phase of devotion has come the inculcating of loyalty, patriotism, reverence, duty, unselfishness, comradeship. With it has also come the veneration of those who have passed from out of the sight of men. It has made itself a religion of Hero Worship, in whose Pantheon God's good man has come to occupy a place that is worshipful. It has

171

made of great men demi-gods; and it has done more than this, for it has served to keep their memories green.

The Shinto faith is the religion of old friends, the religion of lovers, since high among the objects of its homage is fidelity in human affection, unforgetfulness of human ties.

(Treves 1905)

Treves was also sympathetic to the pantheistic component of Shintoism. At William Barnes's school he had acquired not only the naturalist's understanding of nature, but the poet's too. Shintoism's willingness to find God in nature struck a chord in Treves. Thinking he and a Japanese companion were alone while visiting the lonely Shinto temple at Lake Biwa, Treves was surprised to meet an old woman carrying an infant. His companion asked why the old woman was visiting this solitary place. 'She said, "she thought it would do the baby good to see the plum blossom". In such wise commences the education of the Japanese child', Treves wrote. One of the agreeable aspects of *The Other Side of the Lantern* is the fact that while Treves was presented both to the emperor of Japan and the president of the United States on his travels, these events receive scant mention by comparison with such observations on everyday life and ordinary people.

Treves's travel books were usually illustrated by his own competent photographs of the places he visited. An exception was his next book, published in 1907. Commissioned by Macmillans for their enduring *Highways and Byways* series, it was an account of most of the towns and villages of his home county of Dorset, illustrated by Joseph Pennell's fine drawings. Despite the fact that he was close friends with Newman Flower, Treves decided not to publish his third travel book (*Uganda For a Holiday*, 1910) with Cassell, but gave it to Smith, Elder. *The Other Side of the Lantern* had made a great deal of money for Treves and for Cassell. Clearly, the two friends did not see eye to eye on business matters for a period. After Smith, Elder, Treves published with John Murray (*The Land That is Desolate*, 1912). In 1913 Flower wooed Treves back to Cassell for his final four books: *The Country of 'The Ring and Book'* (1913), *The Riviera of the Corniche Road* (1921), *The Lake of Geneva* (1922) and *The Elephant Man and Other Reminiscences* (1923).

The very title of *The Cradle of the Deep* (1908) reflects Treves's boyish notion that 'The fervent spirit of adventure and romance which set aglow the heart of every lad in every town of England, when Elizabeth was queen, found both its source and its end among the West Indies and by the Spanish Main'. Never mind that lack of communication, geographical isolation and the absence of education meant that most boys in Elizabethan England did not even know where either place was; in *The Cradle of the Deep* we are in fantasy land. In one sense, perhaps this is as good a way as any of recounting colonial history if one's aim is not to worry the reader with ugly realities. This fantasy approach to history was something Treves developed here and in *The Riviera of the Corniche Road*; for instance, the 'discovery' of Barbados by Sir Oliver Leigh:

> The ceremony attending the annexation was unaffected. On the beach they put up a cross, to give the function a religious tone, while one of their number carved on the bark of a tree the inscription,
> 'James K. of E. and of this island.'
> The cross was probably made from the staves of a beer barrel, and the graving on the tree, no doubt, was done by a dagger sharpened on a leather jerkin.
>
> (Treves 1908)

Treves's view of the natives was curiously ambivalent. He is appalled by the suffering of a leper colony, and by the overcrowded and unsanitary living conditions in Bridgetown. On the historical question of slavery, he implies that his sympathy is with the slave rather than the master. Looking through some old newspapers in Barbados, he notes that

> The subjoined item from the *Barbados Mercury* of the date of August 4, 1787, is also of interest:
> 'Run away from the subscriber, a tall black man named "Willy": whoever will deliver him to the subscriber shall receive one moidore reward.'
> Now I take the moidore to be equivalent to the sum of twenty-seven shillings, therefore, Willy, in spite of his tallness, would have been little more in value than a pet dog. Indeed, I have seen the reward of two pounds offered for a runaway cat. It is much to be hoped that Willy never came back to the subscriber, but that he hid his pound and a half's worth of flesh in the jungle by the Inland Cliff and there ended his days in peace.

When slavery was abolished, Parliament voted a sum of money to be paid to owners as compensation for setting their slaves at liberty. The total sum thus expended in the salvation of men was nearly nineteen millions sterling. The number of slaves set free was no less than 770,280.

They were probably the only human beings who ever came to know precisely what they were worth, or what was their value in the eyes of others, for in the carrying out of the Act the value of each type of slave had to be defined with great exactness.

(Treves 1908)

Despite his sympathy with the slave, however, Treves had a fairly low opinion of the West Indians. He remarks that 'The negro population of Barbados ... have become, by force of circumstance and against their natural inclination, both a hard-working and a frugal folk', and laments that 'it has come to pass that labour is now not too plentiful in the colony, and the English housewife has begun to experience that dearth of good servants which has long been acute in England'.

Throughout *The Cradle of the Deep* Treves chooses not to approach the West Indies on its own terms (as he was able to do in Japan), but to measure it by English standards. He finds much to criticize; and when he finds something to praise, the praise is limited to the thing being *almost* as good as, or similar to that found in England (or Europe). These criteria are applied to people. For instance, 'The Barbadian negro is a fine specimen of humanity. The man may not be noteworthy, but the woman is a model of anatomical comeliness ... her black face may appear almost beautiful when seen against the pale green background of a thicket of cane'. On another occasion Treves writes that rowing out along Kingston Harbour 'recalls the lazy passage from Venice to Tortello', but 'The gorilla-faced negro, moreover, who grins at the oars is a sorry substitute for the gondolier'. If West Indian people do not quite match up to English ones, neither does the landscape compete, though it is acceptable when reminiscent of, when *almost* like England. So, 'St Kitts has much of the garden trimness of England, and something of the homeliness of the mother country', while Antigua 'is said to be pleasant to live in and to possess scenery very like that of England'.

In *Uganda For a Holiday* (1910) much of the same rhetoric prevails. Treves writes in praise of the Bahima tribe of central Africa that they are 'tall, well-proportioned people, handsome and aristocratic look-

174

ing, whose features are moulded upon lines differing but little from those of the European'; in the Masai 'There is no marked projection of the lower jaw, while the nose is so shapely as to be almost Caucasian'.

Treves has much to say about the Uganda railway ('compared with the immensity of the country through which it passes, it is a mere iron thread across the surface of the world') and the effect it will have on native Ugandans.

When Treves visited the West Indies he saw colonies which had been inhabited by the British for hundreds of years. Europeans had only just penetrated the dark heart of Africa, and it held greater mystery. A man of unusual temper and independent judgement, Treves's views only half conformed with the prevailing sentiments of his class, and he held two species of white man in Uganda in contempt: the big game hunter with his 'small-bore talk', whose 'mental survey could be apparently compressed into the compass of a cartridge case'; and the capitalists who were poised to change forever the face of Africa. Uganda, for centuries impenetrable except on foot, now had a railway. Goods and people could be moved to and from the interior and the coast, and from the coast to the rest of the world. Uganda was about to be 'developed'. This prospect caused Treves to reflect on what would be lost and what would be gained. In native Ugandan society he found a 'natural' form of socialism which he admired for its social organization, but was sceptical of because it avoided 'progress'. He observed that

It would be well if the student of modern politics could visit Rusinga or other villages on the lake [Victoria Nyanza], for in these communities socialism in an ideal form has flourished for unknown centuries. He would find a people who have no rich and no poor, who know nothing either of class distinctions or of privileges, who have (apart from their personal effects) all things more or less in common, and who would appear to be working for the mutual good. In their midst he would come upon no reformer, since there are no oppressed to relieve and no wealthy to rob. He would miss the voice of the preacher, for the people have all settled down to one recognised and one irreducible level, having satisfied themselves that the first duty of man is to live in such a manner as will involve the least amount of labour.

Here, in fact, is socialism *in excelcis*. Here are a people who are free, happy, and contented. That they have made no progress during the last ten or twenty centuries is a matter of little moment, for socialism does not concern itself with the struggle that leads to progress. The primary object of socialism is to maintain the level, the dead low-water level.

The man of enterprise in Rusinga, the man who advocated any advance either personal or communal, the man who introduced the fatal element of competition into this placid spot, would be suppressed as a disturber of the level. For this reason among others the Kavirondo are still living in the Bronze Age, since socialism in its perfected form is nothing if not conservative.

(Treves 1910)

Treves is caught in a liberal dilemma. On the one hand he admires the supposed peacefulness of a socialist society; yet he is too wedded to the notion of competition (founded on individuality) to surrender himself to the communal idea. But the idea of unrestricted competition seems to him barbarous, and he predicts that it will lead to the rape of Uganda – the destruction of a society and the degradation of the individual:

The native of the lake will become in due course civilised, but it is a great leap from the Bronze Age to the twentieth century. It is a change so immense and so abrupt that it is no matter for wonder if in its immediate results there are anomalies and disasters. The village will be broken up; the man – as splendid a specimen of humanity as exists – will lose his cunning as a hunter and his skill with the bow and spear. He will find himself under the influence of a masterful power whose insigne is 'cheap labour'. He will be living not in a thatched hut with the little door at the back, but in a tin shed. As he mounts up into the light he will wear a bowler hat, elastic-side boots and a jersey, with possibly a pair of riding breeches or a mackintosh. Instead of hunting in the jungle or by the lake side, he will be digging drains. He will be told how good it is to work for other people. He will be able not only to get drunk but to become unconscious, and this without difficulty. From the Hindoo trader he will learn dishonesty, lying, and the subtleties of money-lending. So far as he himself is concerned the process of regeneration may be unhappy, but then his son or grandson may blossom into an evangelist.

(Treves 1910)

Perhaps it is this cynicism which had caused Sir Frederick Ponsonby to remark that Treves had 'a certain contempt for the human race' (Ponsonby 1951). But Ponsonby was not quite accurate, for Treves's contempt was more typically reserved for human institutions than for individuals. He disliked systems and slavish devotion to them. Hence his contempt for the continental approach to antisepsis in surgery; fanatical socialism and capitalism were held in equal disregard. So too was much of organized religion. In his discussion of Shintoism Treves expressed his dislike of preaching and 'censoring'; in his forecast for Ugandan capitalism, he sees the debased Ugandan 'evolving' into evangelism.

In *The Land That is Desolate: An Account of a Tour in Palestine* (1912) Treves cannot avoid confronting organized religion and religious strife. At the beginning of the book he asks what the traveller expects from a visit to Palestine:

> As the horizon brightens there will appear the Holy Land ... the place where the Bible was written and where the great religion of the world arose. What does he expect to see emerge from the dull shadow far ahead of the ship's prow? What will he behold that will make this land unlike any other land in the world? ... He expects something uncommon, but unless his mood be very matter-of-fact he must prepare for a great disillusion.
>
> (Treves 1912)

The Land That is Desolate, as the title suggests, is a gloomy book. It has none of the sparkling facetiousness of *The Cradle of the Deep* and makes no concession to the reader. Reviewers disliked its irreverent tone, and while it went through numerous printings, it was never as popular as his other books because Treves dared to ask the simple question, can we take the Bible literally? Many did not like his answer:

> As for the Amorites, the Hittites, and the Jebusites, are they not of the same world as the tribes of Lilliput, and may they not have been encountered by Sinbad the Sailor on his many voyagings? Whatever the fault may be, whether the instruction is given at too impressionable an age, or is conveyed in too spiritual a manner, the fact remains that it is difficult with many to associate the Bible scenes with spots on the solid earth, with places which may be actually reached by steamers and trains,

177

and about which it would not be irreverent to inquire if they afforded convenient hotel accommodation. Thus it is that we are apt for a moment to resent the belief that a hill pointed out by a prosing guide from a railway carriage window is, in all seriousness, the birthplace of Samson, just as we should repudiate the statement that it was the early home of Peter Pan.

(Treves, 1912)

Treves's quarrel is not so much with Christianity, but with the church and with its priests. Of the road from Ekron to Beth-shemesh, along which the chronicles say the Ark of God passed, Treves writes with relief: 'Here at least is the actual scene of an event in Bible history, unspoiled by any church and undefiled by the parade of priestcraft.' For Treves, Palestine is at best as gaudy and vulgar as a fairground, at worst, a cunning fraud practised on the simple faithful. The Via Dolorosa is 'a mere fiction of the Christian Church, a lane of lies, a path of fraud'. Treves believes that Christ did walk the dusty streets of Jerusalem, but he takes comfort in believing that the path is 'buried fathoms beneath dust and stone', and that it 'lies hidden from the eyes of the mumming priest and is safe for ever from that tawdry oblation of gilt image and brazen lamp which marks the Church's appreciation of a sacred place'. In the clearest statement of his own position, Treves writes:

It is an unanswerable testimony to the power and vitality of the Christian faith that it should not only have survived but should have spread itself over the entire earth in spite of the slough of corruption through which the ministers of the Gospel have dragged it ... it seems to be assured that Christianity will outlast both the Christian Church and the self-glorifying inventions of her priests.

(Treves 1912)

By contrast, Treves admires the dignity of the long-suffering Jew who 'should be – although he is not – the rightful inhabitant of Jerusalem'. Of all the monuments in the Holy Land, the Wailing Wall impresses Treves most:

It is an extraordinary and impressive picture. This remnant of a once mighty and arrogant people clamouring outside the wall of their lost Temple; this persistent prayer droned out for wellnigh two thousand years: the wall so terrific, so impassive, so

178

impossible, while those who beat upon it, seeking to come in, are
so feeble and so forlorn. As well one might conceive the picture
of a solitary man kneeling at the foot of a mountain praying that
it may be moved! What an astounding realisation it offers of a
faith that would cleave a barrier of stone, of a longing that can
survive the denial of centuries!

(Treves 1912)

The Land That is Desolate is, apart from *The Other Side of the Lantern*,
the best of Treves's travel books. The quality of Treves's prose varies
directly with the level of anger, pathos or excitement he was experiencing, and Palestine provoked all three. Excitement came at the end
of the journey when he and Annie decided to travel by train from
Damascus to Beirut, from Beirut to Port Said by steamer, and then on
to England. When he tried to buy a ticket, Treves was told that the
line was blocked with snow. 'Determined inquiries,' he wrote, 'as to
when the line would be clear led to no more precise information than
it would be open "soon". "Might it be clear by tomorrow?" "We hope
so." "Might it be blocked for another fortnight?" "Oh, assuredly."'
Most of the Treveses' luggage was at Beirut, but they found Damascus
agreeable enough and resigned to stay until the line cleared.

But next day a large number of pilgrims arrived from Mecca
intending to take the Beirut train. Cholera broke out and the Treveses
had a choice: wait for the Beirut train, knowing that the city might be
quarantined indefinitely; or take the train to Haifa and proceed to
Port Said from there, making arrangements for the luggage to be sent
from Beirut. They opted for the latter. Setting out to purchase tickets,
Treves discovered that

There was a great deal of oriental vagueness about the train. It
was said to leave Damascus at sunrise, but I gathered that the
actual astronomical moment was determined not by the sun but
by the station-master. If that official had had a bad night the
sunrise might be seriously delayed. If, on the other hand, he had
awakened early and was in high spirits he might declare that the
sun was up, while the night was still at its blackest, and
incontinently start the train on its way to the coast.

(Treves 1912)

In order to guard against this eventuality the Treveses took the
precaution of rising at three a.m. on a bitterly cold morning. The

179

already ill-fated journey now became a catalogue of disasters. Riding through the cold streets of Damascus haunted by visions of the poor sleeping in the streets, their cab came to an abrupt halt as a man rose up from the darkness gesticulating wildly. The Treveses thought they were about to robbed, perhaps murdered, but the wild-eyed figure only warned them of an accident up ahead, where a culvert beneath the road had given way and a cab horse had broken a leg.

It was with some relief that they were finally deposited at the station. There was no sign of the train, but the ground appeared littered with bundles. These turned out to be the sleeping forms of the pilgrims who had also decided to take the train rather than risk being quarantined in Damascus. Appreciating the 'oriental vagueness' of the train timetable, they were taking no chances. Moving about the station Treves accidentally awakened one of the sleeping faithful. The consequences were immediate. The entire crowd rose as if in a resurrection scene, gathered its belongings and approached the track. Soon the train approached the station. It had three freight carriages and a first and a third class carriage. When it came to a halt in front of the station the doors opened and out spilled more than a hundred pilgrims from the freight carriages. The train's staff took a leisurely exit from the first-class accommodation.

After much confusion everyone boarded the train. Each of the freight carriages held fifty Russian Moslems, with another forty travelling third class. The Treveses were the only occupants of the first class carriage. At six a.m. the train finally pulled away from Damascus.

The line from Damascus to Haifa was dramatic, with some very steep downhill runs. At around two-thirty in the afternoon, while negotiating one of the steepest parts of the line, the train derailed in spectacular fashion. The Treveses, travelling in the end carriage, only experienced a slight jolt and then a sudden stopping of the train. Treves jumped out to discover that the engine and the tender had plunged over a cliff and lay upside-down, entirely submerged in the river fifty feet below the line. Both the driver and the stoker were thrown clear as the train turned over in mid-air and managed to reach the river bank, but both men were injured. This was more adventure than Treves had bargained for. He immediately joined in the rescue.

The approach to the water's edge was difficult, and still more difficult was the conveying of the injured men up an adjacent

slope. The stoker, who was a Turk, was suffering a good deal
from shock, was badly cut about the head and face and much
bruised elsewhere. The engine-driver, a Bulgarian, was
unhappily in a worse plight, for, in addition to superficial
injuries, it was evident that one of the abdominal organs had
been ruptured. Both of the men were placed lying down in the
compartment next to ours. They were in great pain, but
fortunately I had with me a medicine case and a flask of whisky.
After two doses of morphia they each expressed themselves as
much better. The stoker began to regain his pulse, but the poor
engine-driver, although free from pain, showed no amendment,
and it was evident that, as no operation was possible in this wild
ravine, his case was hopeless.

As to the cause of the accident no light was forthcoming, but it
was quite clear that the carriages had not been struck by any
falling rock as I had supposed. The first of the three goods vans
full of pilgrims was wholly derailed, the front wheels being
within eighteen inches of the edge of the precipice. Had not the
couplings broken the disaster would have been horrible to
contemplate. The front part or bogie of the second van had left
the rails, but the hind wheels still held to the metal and so saved
the whole train, after the couplings had given, from running
headlong over the cliff, for the incline of the road was
considerable.

(Treves 1912)

Treves marvelled at the calm of the Russian pilgrims. Once they
realized they were out of danger and nothing further was to be done,
they set their samovars going to make tea and washed in the river.
The relief train would arrive when it arrived.

It came two and a half hours later in a steady downpour of
rain which made the scene, in Treves's eyes, inexpressibly dismal.
It was the culmination of a series of delays, accidents, mishaps. And
Treves had been forced to confront what had been the bane of his
professional life: a surgical patient who was beyond his skill to
save.

The clearing of the track and the transfer of baggage and pass-
engers was a slow affair. When the time came to move the injured
driver, Treves advised that a makeshift stretcher be fashioned from
the cape of the lone Bedouin on the train. The Russian Moslems

intervened, shouting that he should not be carried lying down because it was bad luck, a portent of death.

> I protested earnestly against this inhuman procedure. I appealed
> to the patient as well as to his friends, but all was in vain; so I
> witnessed the horrible spectacle of a heavy man with a ruptured
> intestine being carried along a very shaky road on another man's
> back, while he was held precariously in place by a third.
>
> (Treves 1912)

Treves had experienced some ugly scenes during the Boer War, but
Annie had never been exposed to anything like this. Treves does not
record her reaction, but the event must have had a great impact on
her. For Treves, it was one of the most miserable experiences of his
life. Finally, at five-thirty p.m. the relief train was ready to depart.
There were no passenger carriages, and the Treveses had to ride in
the guard's van for the eight-and-a-half-hour journey.

> The hours seemed to be interminable. I never looked at my
> watch without being convinced that it had stopped. The night
> was not only dark but very cold, while the pattering of rain on
> the roof of the van made for melancholy. To increase the
> dreariness of the situation there was no light in the van until a
> candle was obtained from the pilgrims. It was stuck in a bottle
> and placed on the floor. It gave a sorry illumination to a sorry
> scene – a bare van with people sitting or lying on the floor in
> company with a dying man and another who was grievously
> injured. I am inclined to think that we should have been better
> without the candle, for there is a negative relief in absolute
> darkness.
>
> (Treves 1912)

Even in this night of despair Treves's sense of humour was not
entirely quenched. Around midnight the train was stopped and a
passenger carriage added. Before they transferred to it, the Treveses
were visited in the guard's van by a group of Turkish railway officials.

> civilities and cards were exchanged through the medium of the
> dragoman. I was wishing that I could speak direct to these
> gentlemen, when one of them came towards me, and, holding
> out his hand, observed with fervour, 'Oh, what a bally country!'.
> It was a somewhat unusual introductory remark, but, assuming
> that the adjective employed had a condemnatory meaning, it

was not entirely out of place, for the night was dark and cold, it was pouring with rain, we were without food or the possibility of obtaining any. I was, however, so delighted to meet a person who spoke English that I grasped this gentleman very warmly by the hand and told him how pleased I was to meet some one I could talk to. To this he replied, 'Oh, what a bally country!'. I agreed with his views as to the immediate country, but, wishing to change the subject, said, 'This has been a most unfortunate accident'. To which he answered, 'Oh, what a bally country!'. I then tried simpler sentences, such as 'Good evening,' 'Are you not wet?', but on each occasion he replied with the criticism, 'Oh, what a bally country!' . . . As he stepped out of the guard's van into the rain I said, 'I'm afraid you will have a very trying journey,' to which he answered, with a smile and a polite bow, 'Oh, what a bally country!'. Thus we parted without further exchange of ideas.

(Treves 1912)

At three a.m. the Treveses reached Haifa and fell gratefully into their beds. After a few hours' sleep Treves rose to visit the engine driver who had been taken to a German hospital in the city. It was a sad end to the journey:

He was conscious, but quite free from pain, and was rapidly nearing the end. His wife was with him. He smiled, as an old friend would smile, when we shook hands, for there was this bond between us – that I had been with him on the train. He nodded as I went out of the room. It was to show that he knew that he was really saying good-bye. He died a little while after I left the ward.

(Treves 1912)

Chapter Twelve

DORSET

After Palestine Treves became more a tourist than a traveller. Palestine had pretty much satisfied his appetite for adventure. He was
sixty now, and his enthusiasm for life undiminished. But, apart from
his visits to the front during the Great War, he would now frequent
the more sedate haunts of the English tourist: Rome, the Riviera and
the Lake of Geneva.

Part of Treves's boyish quality was not only his sense of adventure,
but his desire to invent things, to do things his own way, to make it up.
As a surgeon he was keen to invent appliances and methods; as a
prospective tourist in Italy, he decided to make his own dictionary as
the available ones did not strike him as reliable. Soon after the
Palestine journey the Treveses planned to visit their daughter Enid in
Rome. Newman Flower called in at Thatched House Lodge a few
months before their departure to find Treves busy in his study.

I shall always remember the picture of this room. There were
mounds of papers on the floor. There were loose sheets of notes
scattered on every table and on the chairs. Treves sat in an arm-
chair like an over-worried politician pestered by an avalanche of
documents.

I went to the chair beside him because it was the only chair
clean of papers in the room. 'What is all this?' I asked him
presently, at the end of our preliminary conversation.

'I am making an Italian Dictionary.'

I looked at the *debris*. A master of surgery making a dictionary.

'How long before you finish it?' I inquired.

'God knows.'

'What are you doing it for?'

'Well, whenever I go to Italy, I cannot get a good English–Italian Dictionary, so I am making my own. When I go to Italy next time I shall carry all this clutter with me. In a box. No, in several boxes. Then, when I am bothered with the language, I shall dive through these several boxes to find the right word. I shan't find it. I shall give this dictionary to some Italian station-master as a legacy for his children. Probably he hasn't any children. If he has, then, when Winter comes, these children will light their homely fires with it.'

What he did with that Italian Dictionary I never knew.

(Flower 1950)

As a professional author, Treves was wealthy enough to choose a subject irrespective of its likely sale. In Rome he decided to reconstruct every detail of Robert Browning's long poem, *The Ring and the Book*. He did it more for his own amusement than anything else, but the result was a charming if unusual addition to the Browning literature. Browning was inspired to write the poem when he found an old yellow book with crumpled vellum covers on a market stall in Florence – an account of Count Guido Franceschini's murder of his wife Pomilia and her reputed parents. Treves's scheme was to discover all of the sites where the action of the poem occurred, and to give a fanciful account of the story accompanied by his own delightful photographs. It is a *jeu d'esprit*, an indulgence and a pleasure to read.

Just as Treves put the finishing touches to his book, the Great War began. By the end of the war Treves's Red Cross work had exhausted him. If Palestine had not quite convinced him that he had seen enough of adventure, the Dardanelles did. He spent his days at Thatched House Lodge, continuing to rise before six to write. And he wrote a great deal: observations on the history of medicine, the future of surgery and – the task of those blessed with longer lives – the obituaries of friends and colleagues.

In retirement he resumed a theme which appealed to him as a young medical writer: hygiene. He was one of the first to see the value of preventive medicine, and made suggestions as to how ordinary people could contribute. He wrote tracts against flies, on the proper storage of food and on correct diet. He also became a fervent supporter of the temperance movement, mounting medical arguments against alcohol. These do not always stand up to rigorous scrutiny, and were more inspired by a sense of public duty during wartime than anything else. But his defences of vivisection were to be taken seriously. He was a tough advocate of the practice, upon which medical progress depended. Treves's career as an anatomist had proved to him that, without the countless human dissections he had performed, surgery would still be an uncertain and barbaric craft rather than a science which saved the lives of thousands who would formerly have died.

It was at this time that Treves most appreciated King Edward's gift of Thatched House Lodge in Richmond Park. He marvelled at the variety of bird and animal life and delighted in his garden. One day whilst walking in it, he was approached by a ragged man who asked for money. Recognizing the man's Dorset dialect as near to Dorchester, he inquired in which town he had been born. Learning that the man came from a village he knew well, and that he was down on his luck, Treves promptly employed him as an assistant gardener.

Treves was still active, but his illness during the war had eroded some of his vitality. At sixty-six he decided that, no matter how much he loved Thatched House Lodge, the English climate no longer suited him. Now it was time to retire properly: to bask in the Mediterranean sun and write letters to *The Times* from a deck chair.

There was no definite plan. He and his wife would travel south, live in hotels and move on when the fancy took them. They started at Menton, eighteen miles east of Nice near the Italian border. It had all the right ingredients. There was a castle at the top of the town which once protected it from pirates; there were narrow alleyways, sites of ancient intrigue; the mean temperature was 49°; and a few hours' journey in any direction took one to interesting places.

Lady Treves once said that her husband was never happier than when he had a pen in his hand. In the last three years of his life he published as many books: *The Riviera of the Corniche Road* (1921), *The Lake of Geneva* (1922), and *The Elephant Man and Other Reminiscences* (1923). The first two are more 'bookish' than his previous travel works, relying on amusing retellings of the popular histories which he devoured, supplemented by visits to the sites. But, terse and opinionated to the end, Treves peppered these innocent-looking books with critical observations on contemporary life among the leisured classes in the south of France. Living at Monte Carlo, he was annoyed by the sound of gunfire. On a green below the casino he found 'sportsmen' engaged in the amusement of live pigeon shooting. The pigeons were placed in cages on a semi-circular concrete slab, and released for the pleasure of well-heeled gunslingers. His angry letter to *The Times* and this passage from *The Riviera of the Corniche Road* would have confused the anti-vivisectionists of the day, who saw him as an animal murderer:

> In pigeon shooting from traps there is not the faintest element of sport. It is merely an exhibition of mean brutality which is totally opposed to the British conception of sport and it is gratifying to note that among the competitors in this contemptible game an English name is uncommon. The terrified pigeon pegged out to be shot at has practically no chance, while the skill displayed by the most apt of the pseudo-sportsmen is of a paltry order.
>
> (Treves 1921)

If Monte Carlo was fun but essentially shallow, Menton was pretty but ultimately dull. Treves thought the place to be marked

> by a respectability which is commendable, but at the same time almost awe-inspiring. . . . If Monte Carlo be a town of scarlet silks, short skirts and high-heeled shoes, Menton is a town of alpaca and cotton gloves and of skirts so long that they almost hide the elastic-side boots.
>
> (Treves 1921)

It was full of English 'aunts' who 'fill the frivolous bachelor with reverential alarm'.

So, tiring of Menton, it was back to Monte Carlo. It was there that Treves probably saw his last patient – a distinguished general from the Great War who was dying of cancer. He was being nursed in a convent, and when the ever-patriotic Lord Northcliffe heard of this he decided that the general must be moved at once to the best hospital in Paris. He ordered a private train to collect him from Menton. Newman Flower describes Treves's reaction to this news:

> Treves heard of this a few hours before the train was due to start. He said to me:
> 'I knew I must go and see this sportsman (the French doctor). General —— would be dead before the train got to Nice, and a fine scandal for the British Government if his dead body was dragged out of the train at Paris.'
> So he went to visit the sick man . . . who had given the fullness

of his Life to the nation. Dying as the hours passed, while he watched with vacant stare the Sisters who prayed for him.

Treves gave me the picture of that room. The General was lying in agony, with the sweat of pain rolling down his livid face. He stared with large strained eyes at nothing, whilst a Sister prayed openly in a corner of the room.

Treves went up to him. Presently the sufferer recognised him. He was a friend – a man he knew. And out of his pain he gave one imploring cry: .

'Give me a . . . . revolver that I may shoot my bloody self.'

'Hush,' came the quiet voice of the Sister. 'It is only dogs that are shot.'

Treves touched the sleeve of the Sister. He led her out of the room.

'Sister,' he said – and this is what he told me – 'You can only do a little service for that man, and I beg you to do it. He is dying, and not all your prayers can save him. But you have got it in your power to help his passing. Get a bottle of good port wine and put it by his side. And a glass. And put a pack of cards in his hand – let him play with them. Let him feel them. It will make his passing easy.'

Not many hours later one of Britain's most eminent military figures died with the cards in his hands and a half-finished bottle of port by his side.

Such was the human understanding of Frederick Treves.

(Flower 1950)

In 1921 and 1922 Treves lived at Evian and Vevey, passing his days in reading and writing, swimming and walking. On 2 October 1922 Buckingham Palace announced that Treves's intended visit to London was postponed indefinitely as he was laid up at Montreux with acute pleurisy. He missed old friends; and he missed Dorset. In April 1923 he wrote to Newman Flower:

Dorset will be very beautiful now. How I would like to get back and wander in her woods! When I was fourteen I cut my initials on a tree in the woods beside Came Golf Links. I went there recently and looked for the tree, and I found it, and the 'F.T.' as I cut it. And that was in '67.

Flower later wrote that

As the years closed about him this passion for Dorset seemed to become that of a lover for a maid. He appeared to grow younger with these last years, as if something in him turned again to youth. The human understanding became more accentuated, and the kindliness in the heart of him clear like an outstanding jewel.

(Flower 1950)

In the spring of 1923, done with Buckingham Palace formality, Treves turned up in London unannounced. He wanted to see old friends, to see Dorset. But as soon as he arrived he was taken ill and brought to a London nursing home. For four weeks he was too ill to see anyone. Then he wrote to Flower. He was weak, but his indomitable humour prevailed:

> I have had a rotten time. I was 'took' nearly a month ago, and have been in this Home three weeks. I was suddenly clutched in the middle of the night. The pain was very bad, and the nights hideous. I had what the seamen of Drake's day would term 'a close call'. The question was raised as to the excision of the gall-bladder. Three of the best men in London discussed this proposal over my indifferent body late at night. Their speech reminded me of the pirates in Stevenson's *Treasure Island*, for the gist of it was: 'Let us cut his gall-bladder out. What ho! and a bottle of rum!' However, they agreed to wait, so we 'cast four anchors out of the stern', and hoped for the day!

For the first time in his life, Treves knew what it was like to be on the other end of surgical deliberation. He did not find it a pleasant experience.

After a few weeks Treves decided to return to Vevey. He continued to swim and walk, and worked busily on *The Elephant Man* – his greatest book. Feeling stronger, he returned in November to deliver the manuscript to Newman Flower. They shared a memorable lunch with Edmund Gosse, author of the classic autobiography *Father and Son*. It was a simple meal – cold grouse and claret – but Flower remembered it as 'the happiest lunch in my life, and if I lived a thousand years I should never know another like it'. Treves and Gosse 'flung anecdote against anecdote', with Flower laughing helplessly until tears filled his eyes. Treves described the sexual habits of the pigeons who frequented his window sill at Vevey. Gosse desribed

189

being stunned by a sepulchral voice exclaiming behind him in Rome, 'the Vatican will hold no secrets from me!' – it was the novelist Hall Caine, posturing in a wide-brimmed hat. The next morning Treves took the boat train back to Vevey.

Later in November the Treveses moved to Montreux. One day in December he decided to watch a game of football. He was never particularly fond of the game; it was an act of idleness, a whiling away of the time. It began to snow during the match, but Treves stayed to the end. When he returned to his hotel he had caught a chill. By evening Lady Treves was worried. A doctor was called. The doctor ordered no food. Treves smiled but was worried. He himself had given the order countless times: it was a precaution against aggravating peritonitis. In the morning he violently demanded his breakfast. If it was not brought at once, he would get it himself. His condition deteriorated quickly. He became delirious, babbling continuously about blue trains.

On the morning of 7 December he was taken to the Clinique de Rosemont at Lausanne. He died later that day. Peritonitis. He would have laughed at the irony of it.

The irony is compounded by the fact that he was *the* expert on peritonitis. His daughter Hetty had died of it because he had operated too late. Then he had saved King Edward from it by operating in time. No post-mortem was performed, so it is impossible to determine the precise cause of the peritonitis. G. E. Moloney speculated in 1962 that it was probably caused by a perforated gall-bladder. But historians Owen and Sarah Wangensteen offered a possible diagnosis in 1978 which Treves would have found much more apt. They ask:

> Could incomplete cecal descent, a clinical entity defined by
> Treves, attended by appendical obstruction, have accounted for
> the peritonitis that took his life? It has been suggested that the
> peritonitis was biliary in origin. But certainly rupture of the
> appendix is a far more frequent cause of peritonitis than is
> cholecystitis.
>
> (Wangensteen and Wangensteen 1978)

Lady Treves was alone in Montreux and had no one to comfort her or to assist with the arrangements. She contacted Newman Flower, who arranged for notices in the press. Lady Treves herself had Frederick cremated at Lausanne. She would send the ashes to

England by train, and Flower would see that they were buried in Dorchester cemetery. She would remain behind in Montreux.

Flower announced that the funeral would take place in Dorchester on 2 January 1924. But on the last day of December there was a violent snowstorm on the continent, and trains were delayed. To make matters worse, Treves's ashes were lost. Flower sent eighteen cables that day to stations in France and Switzerland. If he could not locate them, the funeral would have to be rescheduled. Buckingham Palace and Marlborough House would have to be notified. The inconvenience would be colossal. The whole business infuriated Flower because he was a stickler for deadlines. As a publisher, only two things mattered: good copy, and good copy delivered on time. Treves was rare as an author in that he always delivered both. Now he would be late for his own funeral, and Flower would be to blame. Resigned, he contacted Buckingham Palace and Marlborough House and told them the funeral was postponed indefinitely.

No sooner had he done this than a message arrived that the ashes were at Rotherhithe. He sent a messenger at once to collect them. Breathing a great sigh of relief and swallowing his pride, he phoned the royal residences again. An hour later the messenger arrived – without the ashes. Without a death certificate the customs officials would not release them. This was impossible. Flower had no idea where the certificate might be, except with the doctor in Lausanne, or with Lady Treves. He was now at his wits' end.

> I picked up the telephone to speak to the Court and postpone the funeral again; then put it down. One could not play Box and Cox with the Court in this fashion. Instead, I sent the messenger back to Rotherhithe to inform the Customs that the King was sending Lord Dawson to Dorchester to be present at this funeral in two days' time, and if they held back the ashes then they would have to explain. I cabled to Lady Treves for the Death Certificate, and, with the aid of the Dorset Society, I obtained from the Home Office a special order to 'bury'.
>
> (Flower 1950)

Treves's ashes finally arrived on New Year's Day, 1924, at St Peter's, Dorchester. They were contained in a simple bronze casket with the inscription, 'Frederick Treves, 1853–1923'.

It was bitterly cold on 2 January, and Dorchester was swept with a blinding rain. The sad procession that filed into St Peter's was one of

the most distinguished the town had ever seen. Lord Dawson represented King George, who sent a large bouquet. Queen Alexandra,
represented by Lord Howe, sent a large cross of flowers with the
inscription, 'For my beloved Sir Frederick Treves, whom we all loved
so dearly and now will miss so sadly, from his affectionate Alexandra,
Sandringham, Norfolk'. The Lord Lieutenant, the Earl of Shaftes-
bury was there, as were friends from the medical profession, the Red
Cross, the army and a host of private mourners.

The service was arranged by Thomas Hardy. Hardy and Treves
were intimate not simply because of their personal friendship, but
because of their rootedness in the Dorset soil, and their common
descent through the teaching of William Barnes. Hardy included the
Tate and Brady version of the Ninetieth Psalm, sung to the tune of St
Stephen – an old Dorset tradition which Hardy remembered from his
father's funeral. The Society of Dorset Men affixed to their wreath a
verse from William Barnes, in the Dorset dialect that could reduce the
sometimes gruff Treves to tears:

> An' oft do come a saddened hour
>   When there must go away
> Woone well beloved to our heart's core
>   Vor long, perhaps vor aye.
> An' oh! it is a touchen thing
>   The loven heart must rue
> To hear behind his last farewell
>   The geate a-vallen to!

Hardy was then eighty-four and frail, and Flower had phoned in the
morning begging him not to come to the funeral in the cold rain. But
Hardy would have none of it. He stood beside the open grave for the
entire ceremony without an umbrella, hat in hand, shivering with
cold and the rain running under his collar.

After the funeral Hardy entertained guests to tea. He reminisced
how his father and Treves's had been friends, how his first writing
desk – which he still had – was purchased from Treves's father. He
told the story of Treves hiding behind the coats at William Barnes's
school, too shy to come out until the maid arrived to take him home.
He described the evenings they spent reminiscing of old Dorset when
Treves rented a summer house near Hardy; and how the Society of
Dorset Men chose Treves as their first president and Hardy as their
second – a measure of the respect in which he was held.

The following Saturday a poem by Hardy appeared in *The Times* – a 'last tribute to an old friend', and a fitting epitaph for an extraordinary man.

In The Evening

In Memoriam Frederici Treves, 1853–1923
(Dorchester Cemetery)

In the evening, shortly after he was dead,
   He lay amid the dust and hoar
Of ages, and to a spirit attending said,
     'This chalky bed? –
   I seem to have been here before?'

'O yes – you *have* been here. You knew the place,'
   The sprite replied, 'long ere your call;
And if you cared to do so you might trace
     In this white space
   Your quality, your substance, and your all.'

Thereat he said: 'Why was I called away?
   I felt no trouble or discontent.
Why did I not prolong my ancient stay
     Herein for aye?'
   The sprite looked vague. 'None knows!
    You went.

'True, Time has not as yet revealed to you
   Your need to go. But, some men tell,
A marvellous Deftness called you forth – to do
     Much that was due.
   Good. You have returned. And all is well.'

A NOTE ON SOURCES

The full bibliography of works by Treves should assist those who wish to explore his views in greater detail. Secondary sources are cited within the text, and there is a full bibliography of works consulted.

The relevant reports on the Royal Commission inquiries into the Boer War are Cd 230 (1900); Cd 453 (1901); Cd 455 (1901); Cd 791 (1901); Cd 1791 (1903).

Documents cited in the Royal Archive at Windsor are RA/X40/28, RA/W77/84, RA/W77/50 and King George V Diary RA.

BIBLIOGRAPHY OF WORKS
BY
SIR FREDERICK TREVES

ABBREVIATIONS

BMJ	*British Medical Journal*
LHG	*London Hospital Gazette*
MCT	*Medico-Chirurgical Transactions*
TCSL	*Transactions of the Clinical Society of London*
TPSL	*Transactions of the Pathological Society of London*

1872

'The relationship between the odour of gases and their power of resisting liquefaction', *Pharamceutical Journal and Transactions* 3: 181–2.

1876

'The psychology of general paralysis of the insane', *Journal of Psychological Medicine* 2: 296–302.

1877

'Anaemia treated by transfusion: A case of failure', *Lancet* 1: 833–4.
'Cheyne-Stokes' respiration', *Lancet* 1: 481.

1878

'The function of the frontal lobes of the brain, as illustrated by a case of injury', *Lancet* 1: 344–6, 378–80.
'The physiology of some phases of the poetic mind', *Journal of Mental Science* 24: 64–75, 233–43.

1879

'Carcinoma of the oesophagus', *Lancet* 1: 475–6.
'Mr. Hutchinson's clinique', *Lancet* 1: 298–9.
'Popliteal aneurism', *Lancet* 2: 9.
'Surgical cases and clinical remarks', *Lancet* 2: 613.

1880

'Registration of diseases in hospitals' (letter), *Lancet* 2: 119.

'Suprapubic puncture of the bladder' (letter), *Lancet* 2: 400.

1881

'A case illustrating the condition of large arteries after ligature under antiseptic and non-antiseptic measures', *BMJ* 1: 232–3.

'Case of strangulated congenital umbilical hernia', *Lancet* 1: 323–4.

'Case of villous polyp of the bladder', *TPSL* 32: 141–2.

'Catgut ligature in the treatment of aneurism', *Lancet* 1: 558.

'Dissection of a congenital hydrocele of the neck', *TPSL* 32: 194–7.

'A lecture on the pathology of scrofulous lymphatic glands', *BMJ* 1: 675–9.

'Ostitis deformans', *TPSL* 32: 167–9.

'Tubercle: Its histological characters and its relation to the inflammatory process as shown in tuberculosis of lymphatic glands', *International Congress of Medicine* 1: 298–303.

'Varicose veins of abdominal wall', *BMJ* 2: 597.

'Vesical calculus from a dog', *TPSL* 32: 311.

1882

'Congenital coccygeal tumour. Attached foetus', *TPSL* 33: 285–8.

The Dress of the Period in its Relation to Health, London: Allman & Son.

'Excision of the entire tongue by Whitehead's method', *Lancet* 1: 641–2.

'Perforating ulcer of the foot and progressive locomotor ataxia', *Lancet* 2: 653–4.

'Phosphorous necrosis' (letter), *Lancet* 1: 206.

Scrofula and Its Gland Diseases: An Introduction to the General Pathology of Scrofula, With an Account of the Histology, Diagnosis and Treatment of its Glandular Affections, London: Smith, Elder; New York: Birmingham & Co.; Philadelphia, PA: H. C. Lea's Son & Co. (1883).

1883

'Congenital malformation of the skull', *TPSL* 34: 228.

'Four cases of excision of the entire tongue by scissors', *Lancet* 1: 677–8.

'The influence of dress on health' in M. Morris (ed.), *The Book of Health*, London: 461–517.

'On resection of portions of intestine', *MCT* 66: 55–67.

'On the entrance of air into veins during operations', *BMJ* 1: 1278–9.

'On the treatment of certain fractures of the lower end of the femur', *BMJ* 1: 306–8.

'Scrofula' in T. Holmes and J. W. Hulke (eds.) *A System of Surgery*, 3rd ed., London: Longmans & Co.

Scrofula and Its Gland Diseases, Philadelphia, PA: H. C. Lea's Son & Co.

'Sebaceous cysts of the hand', *BMJ* 2: 1123–4.

Surgical Applied Anatomy, London: Cassell & Co.; Philadelphia, PA: H. C. Lea's Son & Co.

1884

'Actinomycosis', *BMJ* 1: 61.

'A case of giant growth of the lower limb', *BMJ* 1: 1147.

'A case of supposed actinomycosis', *TPSL* 35: 356–62.
'Congenital deformity', *BMJ* 2: 1140.
'The direct treatment of psoas abscess with caries of the spine', *MCT* 67: 113–26.
'The element of pain in intestinal obstruction', *BMJ* 2: 62–4.
Intestinal Obstruction: Its Varieties, With Their Pathology, Diagnosis, and Treatment, London: Cassell & Co.; Philadelphia, PA: H. C. Lea's Son & Co.
'Malformations and diseases of the spine' in J. Ashhurst (ed.) *The International Encyclopaedia of Surgery*, vol. 4, London.
'On certain forms of intestinal obstruction that may follow after hernia', *BMJ* 1: 669.
'Treatment of perforating ulcer of the foot', *Lancet* 2: 949–51.

1885

'Two cases of primary tumour of the soft palate', *TPSL* 36: 397–8.
'Acute peritonitis treated by abdominal section', *MCT* 68: 175–84.
The Anatomy of the Intestinal Canal and Peritoneum in Man, London: H. K. Lewis.
'A case of congenital deformity', *TPSL* 36: 494–8.
'A case of scrofulous gland-disease with phthisis', *BMJ* 1: 231.
'Hernia at the seat of an artificial anus', *Lancet* 2: 525–6.
'Lectures on the anatomy of the intestinal canal and peritoneum in man', *BMJ* 1: 415–19, 470–4, 580–3.
'Malformations and diseases of the head', in J. Ashhurst (ed.) *The International Encyclopaedia of Surgery*, vol. 5, London.
'On faecal accumulation', *Lancet* 2: 1133–5.
'The operative treatment of intestinal obstruction', *BMJ* 2: 387–90.
'Resection of the intestine', *BMJ* 1: 657.
'Strangulated omental hernia' (letter), *Lancet* 1: 772.
'Treatment of intestinal obstruction', *Lancet* 1: 40.
'The treatment of intussusception', *Proceedings of the Medical Society of London* 8: 83–94.
'The treatment of obstinate constipation', *BMJ* 2: 892–3.
'Two cases of injury by exploding dynamite', *BMJ* 1: 329.

1886

'Vices de conformation et affections de la colonne vertébrale' in *Encyclopédie Internationale de Chirurgie*, vol. 5, Paris: J.-B. Baillière & Fils.
'Malformations et maladies de la tête' in *Encyclopédie Internationale de Chirurgie*, vol. 5, Paris: J.-B. Baillière & Fils.
'Abdominal hernia', 'Air in veins', 'Artificial anus', 'Colectomy', 'Colotomy', 'Diaphragmatic hernia', 'Enterectomy', 'Enterotomy', 'Faecal abscess and faecal fistula', 'Femoral hernia', 'Hernia, inflamed', 'Hernia, obstructed or incarcerated', 'Hernia, strangulated', 'Inguinal hernia', 'Intestinal obstruction', 'Laparotomy for intestinal obstruction', 'Lumbar hernia', 'Lymphadenitis or adenitis', 'Lymphadenoma', 'Lymphangiectasis and lymphangioma', 'Lymphangitis, or

angioleucitis', 'Lymphorrhoea or lymphorrhagia', 'Obturator hernia',
'Perineal hernia', 'Pudendal hernia', 'Thoracic duct, injuries and
diseases of', 'Umbilical hernia', 'Vaginal hernia', in C. Heath (ed.)
Dictionary of Practical Surgery, 2 vols, London.

'Abstracts of six lectures on the intestinal canal and peritoneum in
mammalia', *BMJ* 1: 638–40.

'A case of acute myositis', *TCSL* 20: 84–90.

'A case of haemophilia: pedigree through five generations', *Lancet* 2: 533–4.

'A case of pulsating tumour of the head with Raynaud's disease', *TCSL* 20:
12–21.

'A degree for London medical students' (letter), *BMJ* 2: 999.

'Diseases of the head' in F. Treves (ed.) *A Manual of Surgery*, London:
Cassell & Co., 365–79.

'Haemophilia' in F. Treves (ed.) *A Manual of Surgery*, London: Cassell &
Co., 236–9.

'Hysteria' in F. Treves (ed.) *A Manual of Surgery*, London: Cassell & Co.,
210–15.

The Influence of Clothing on Health, London: Cassell & Co.

'Injuries and diseases of the female generative organs' in F. Treves (ed.) *A
Manual of Surgery*, London: Cassell & Co., pp 377–434.

'The iodoform rash', *Practitioner* 37: 271–8.

A Manual of Surgery (ed.), London: Cassell & Co.

'Rest in the treatment of scrofulous neck', *Lancet* 1: 1060–2.

'Severe urethral stricture treated by permanent supra-pubic drainage of
the bladder', *Lancet* 1: 1161–2.

'The treatment of fractures of the patella', *BMJ* 2: 153–4.

1887

'Hernia of the caecum', *Proceedings of the Medical Society of London* 10: 11–24.

'Malignant cysts of the neck', *TPSL* 38: 360–73.

'Richter's hernia or partial enterocele', *MCT* 70: 149–67.

'A case of general tuberculosis', *Lancet* 1: 18–19.

'Case of simple fracture of the skull with a puffy tumour', *BMJ* 1: 934–5.

'Clinical lectures on a case of removal of the kidney together with both
ovaries', *Lancet* 2: 603–4.

'A form of glandular swelling that is cured by arsenic', *TCSL* 20: 176–80.

'A gluteal trochanter in the human subject', *Journal of Anatomy* 21: 325–7.

'On the anatomy of the sondaic rhinoceros' (with F. E. Beddard),
Transactions of the Zooligical Society of London 12: 183–98.

'A sixteenth century amputation', *Lancet* 1: 63–4.

'Treatment of wounds', *BMJ* 1: 938.

'An unusual case of scirrhus of the breast', *Lancet* 2: 520–1.

'Address to the Royal National Mission to Deep Sea Fishermen', *Toilers of
the Deep* 2: 134.

'Minute from council meeting of the Royal National Mission to Deep Sea
Fishermen', *Toilers of the Deep* 2: 247.

1888

Darmobstruction: Ihre Arten, sowie ihre Pathologie, Diagnose und Therapie,
Leipzig: Arnold.
'Congenital cartilaginous tumour of the neck', *TPSL* 39: 297–9.
'The diagnosis and treatment of chronic intestinal obstruction', *Proceedings
of the Medical Society of London* 11: 21–32.
'Peculiar mode of rupture of a hydatid cyst', *TCSL* 21: 82–6.
'Sarcomatous tumour of the sole of the foot', *TPSL* 39: 308–11.
'Stricture of the intestine following tubercular ulcer', *TPSL* 39: 113–17.
'Acute suppuration of the knee-joint treated by continued irrigation', *BMJ*
2: 8–10.
'A case of cephalhaematoma with extensive ossification of the cyst wall',
TCSL 21: 22–5.
'A case of suppurative synovitis treated by drainage of the knee-joint',
Lancet 1: 676.
'Clinical lecture on hernia into the foramen of Winslow', *Lancet* 2: 701–4.
'Horny tumour in a mouse', *TPSL* 39: 463.
'Relapsing typhlitis treated by operation', *MCT* 71: 165–72.
Surgical Applied Anatomy, 2nd ed., London: Cassell & Co; Philadelphia, PA:
Lea Bros & Co.
'The treatment of carotid haemorrhage', *Proceedings of The Medical Society of
London* 11: 115–19.
'Vascular tumours of the mouth and tongue', *TPSL* 39: 97–101.

1889

'A case of relapsing typhlitis treated by removal of the vermiform
appendix' (with James Dodd Swallow), *Lancet* 1: 267–9.
'A discussion on the medical treatment of typhlitis', *BMJ* 2: 1030–4.
'On the anatomy of *Rhinoceros sumantrensis*', *Proceedings of the Zoological Society
of London*, pp 7–25.
'A successful case of Loreta's operation on the stomach', *BMJ* 1: 1105–7.
'Treatment of scrofulous glands', *Lancet* 2: 582–4.

1890

'Clinical lecture on a case of cyst of the pancreas', *Lancet* 2: 655–7.
A German–English Dictionary of Medical Terms (with Hugo Lang), London:
J. & A. Churchill; Philadelphia, PA: Blakiston, Son & Co.
'Recurrent appendicitis' (letter), *Lancet* 2: 792.
The Surgical Treatment of Typhlitis, London: John Bale & Sons.
'The treatment of prolapse of the rectum by excision', *Lancet* 1: 396–7,
454–5.

1891

'The debate on typhlitis at the clinical society' (letter), *Lancet* 1: 458.
A Manual of Operative Surgery, 2 vols, London: Cassell & Co.
'The surgical treatment of typhlitis' in *Wood's Medical and Surgical
Monographs*, 11: 513–38.
'Two cases of amputation of the entire upper extremity', *Lancet* 2: 1158–9.

1892

'A case of contracted knee treated by tenotomy by the open method',
Lancet 2: 1161.

'A case of sarcoma of the buttock treated by ligature of the internal iliac
artery', *TCSL* 25: 249–52.

'A clinical lecture on the treatment of spinal and other tubercular
diseases', *Lancet* 1: 1122–5.

'A clinical lecture on some aspects of chronic intestinal obstruction',
Clinical Journal 1: 102–5.

'Phosphorous necrosis of the upper jaw; chronic abscess of the brain',
Lancet 2: 1439–40.

'Physical education' in T. Stevenson and S. F. Murphy (eds.) *A Treatise on
Hygiene and Public Health*, vol. 1, London: 537–613.

Physical Education, London: J. & A. Churchill; Philadelphia, PA:
P. Blakiston, Son & Co.

The Student's Handbook of Surgical Operations, London: Cassell & Co.;
Philadelphia, PA: Lea Bros & Co.

'Surgery of the appendix vermiformis' (letter), *Medical News* (NY) 61: 531.

Surgical Applied Anatomy, 3rd ed., London: Cassell & Co.; Philadelphia, PA:
Lea Bros & Co.

Annals of Surgery (Philadelphia, PA), joint editor from vol. 15 (1892) to vol.
22 (1895).

'The new hospital ship the *Alice Fisher*', *Toilers of the Deep* 7: 65–6.

1893

'The abdominal viscera' in H. Morris (ed.) *A Treatise on Human Anatomy*,
London, pp. 989–1041.

'A case of lipoma of the broad ligament', *TCSL* 26: 101–4.

'A case of removal of a portion of the sigmoid flexure', *Lancet* 1: 521–2.

'A clinical lecture on haemorrhoids', *Clinical Journal* 3: 116–21.

'The employment of iodoform in abdominal operations', *Lancet* 1: 1375–7.

'A method of treating compound fractures', *Annals of Surgery* 17: 140–6.

'Remarks on a case of epithelioma of the rectum: Its diagnosis and
treatment', *Clinical Journal* 1: 221–2.

'A series of cases of relapsing typhlitis treated by operation', *BMJ* 1:
835–7.

'Tenotomy by the old method', *American Journal of the Medical Sciences* 105:
15–20.

1894

'A case of "suppurative pylephlebitis" in which laparotomy was
performed', *Lancet* 1: 663–5.

'The club's union dinner', *LHG* 1: 33.

'Demonstration of the Hyderabad method of chloroform administration',
LHG 1: 29.

'On peritonitis', *Transactions of the Medical Society of London* 17: 125–95.

'Our annual dinner and re-union of old students', *LHG* 1: 50.

'The treatment of tuberculous peritonitis', *Annals of Surgery* 19: 619–30.

1895

'Abdominal section for intestinal stricture', *Medical Press* 60: 393–4.

'Abdominal section for long-standing pain in the stomach with obscure symptoms simulating gastric ulcer', *Medical Press* 60: 394.

'An address on the surgical aspect of tuberculosis', *Lancet* 2: 1030–4.

'A case illustrating an early stage of hernia of the bladder', *Lancet* 1: 1424.

'A clinical lecture on cancer of the rectum', *Clinical Journal* 5: 330–5.

'Fond delusions', *LHG* 2: 4–5.

A System of Surgery, 2 vols (ed.), London: Cassell & Co.; Philadelphia, PA: Lea Bros & Co. Treves's articles include 'Haemophilia', 'Hysteria in its Surgical Relations', 'The Influence of Constitutional Conditions Upon Injuries', 'Tuberculosis', 'Hernia', 'Injuries and Diseases of the Abdomen'.

'Murphy's button', *Practitioner* 54: 481–6.

'Observations on a further series of cases of relapsing typhlitis treated by operation', *BMJ* 1: 517–19.

'Presentation to Dr Hughlings Jackson and presentation of prizes', *LHG* 2: 52.

The Surgical Treatment of Perityphlitis, 2nd ed., London: John Bale & Sons.

1896

'Anaesthetics in operative surgery', *Practitioner* 57: 377–83.

'Clubs' union annual dinner', *LHG* 3: 39.

'A group of twenty-seven abdominal operations', *Lancet* 1: 15–18.

'A review of the surgery of the peritoneum', *BMJ* 2: 1305–8.

'The treatment of Glenard's disease by abdominal section, with some comments upon intestinal neuroses', *BMJ* 1: 1–4.

'Two cases of pulmonary abscess treated by operation', *Lancet* 2: 532–4.

1897

'Acute peritonitis' in T. C. Allbutt (ed.) *A System of Medicine*, vol. 3, London.

'The annual diner for old "London" men', *LHG* 4: 61.

'Enteroptosis' in T. C. Allbutt (ed.) *A System of Medicine*, vol. 4, London.

'Intestinal obstruction' in T. C. Allbutt (ed.) *A System of Medicine*, vol. 4, London.

'Perityphlitis' in T. C. Allbutt (ed.) *A System of Medicine*, vol. 4, London.

Perityphlitis and Its Varieties: Their Pathology, Clinical Manifestations, and Treatment, London: Macmillan & Co.

'The preparation for an operation by a private nurse', *LHG* 4: 89.

'The progress of surgery', *Practitioner* 58: 619–30.

1898

'Abdominal section as a medical measure', *Transactions of Medical Society of London* 21: 220–36.

'An address on some rudiments of intestinal surgery', *BMJ* 2: 1385–90.

'Iodopathic dilatation of the colon, illustrated by a case in which the entire rectum, sigmoid flexure, and descending colon were excised', *Lancet* 1: 276–9.

1899

'A case of jaundice of sixteen years' standing treated by operation', *Practitioner* 62: 18–20.

'"Going to Table Bay." I: On going to the Wars' (letter), *LHG* 6: 124–5.

Intestinal Obstruction, 2nd ed., London: Cassell & Co.; New York: W. Wood & Co.

1900

'Address to the Royal National Mission to Deep Sea Fishermen', *Toilers of the Deep* 15: 163.

'After Spion Kop', *BMJ* 1: 599–600.

'Albert Ernest Elliott, M.A. Cantab. M.R.C.S., L.R.C.P., Civil Surgeon, Field Force, South Africa' (obituary), *BMJ* 2: 1900, 1752.

'The Battle of Spion Kop', *BMJ* 1: 534–5.

'The Battle of Tugela (Colenso)', *BMJ* 1: 219–21.

'Christmas with the Field Force', *LHG* 6: 157–8.

'A clinical lecture on ptosis of the liver and the "floating lobe"', *Lancet* 1: 1339–44.

'Ladies in South Africa' (letter), *The Times* 14 July: 10.

'Letters from the Front', *LHG* 6: 177–8.

'The march to the Tugela', *BMJ* 1: 470–1.

'Medical arrangements at the Cape' (two letters, one co-authored by Sir William MacCormack), *The Times* 2 May: 8.

'Medical arrangements in South Africa' (letter), *BMJ* 1: 1611–12.

'The medical services in the South African War' (letter), *The Times* 30 April: 6.

'Mr Treves and explosive bullets', *The Times* 9 March: 5.

'Mr Treves on the military hospitals', *The Times* 29 June: 12.

'A mobile hospital in Natal', *BMJ* 1: 914–15.

'Nurses at the Front', *The Times* 30 January: 6.

'On the wounded in the Transvaal War', *MCT* 83: 271–94.

'The opening of the new clubs' union rooms, garden and fives court, and distribution of prizes', *LHG* 7: 75–6.

'The Rampley dinner', *LHG* 7: 116.

'The relief of Ladysmith', *BMJ* 1: 862–5.

'The retreat from Spearman's Hill to Chieveley', *BMJ* 1: 726–7.

'A so-called "Interview"', *BMJ* 2: 769.

'Spion Kop and after', *LHG* 6: 199–200.

'The surgeon in the nineteenth century', *BMJ* 2: 284–9.

The Tale of a Field Hospital, London: Cassell & Co.

'Three cases in which moveable kidney produced all the symptoms of gall-stones' (with T. J. Maclagan), *Lancet* 1: 15–17.

1901

'The medical profession', *BMJ* 2: 1375–6.

'Nursing at the Front' (letter), *Daily Chronicle* 21 January: 3.

'The reorganization of the army medical services' (letter), *The Times* 2 November: 10.

'The South African Hospitals Commission', *Nineteenth Century and After*, 49: 396–405.

Surgical Applied Anatomy, 4th ed. (with Arthur Keith), London: Cassell & Co.

1902

'Anti-vivisection methods' (letter), *The Times* 18 April: 6.

'The Cavendish Lecture on some phases of inflammation of the appendix', *BMJ* 1: 1589–94.

Intestinal Obstruction, 3rd ed., London: Cassell & Co.; New York: W. Wood & Co.

'A modern religio medici', *BMJ* 2: 1197–9.

'Remarks on the surgical treatment of arterio-venous aneurysm', *BMJ* 1: 1133–5.

'Sir F. Treves on surgery', *The Times* 11 October: 8.

'Sir Frederick Treves on the romance of medicine', *The Times* 13 June: 4.

Surgical Applied Anatomy, 4th ed. (with Arthur Keith), Philadelphia, PA: Lea Bros & Co.

1903

'The duration of life after gastrostomy for cancer of the oesophagus' (letter), *BMJ* 1: 1432.

'The London Hospital' (letter), *The Times* 23 January: 8.

'The London Hospital Medical College Endowment Fund' (letter with S. A. T. Yates and W. D. Hoare), *LHG* 9: 133–4.

A Manual of Operative Surgery, 2nd ed., 2 vols (with Jonathan Hutchinson, Jr), London: Cassell & Co.; Philadelphia, PA: Lea Bros & Co.

'The mimicry of gastric troubles by spinal disease', *Practitioner* 70: 1–5.

'Sir Frederick Treves and the advance of surgical science', *The Times* 25 February: 14.

'Thomas John Maclagan, M.D. Edin., Physician-in-Ordinary to Prince and Princess Christian of Schleswig-Holstein' (obituary), *BMJ* 1: 766.

1904

'The importance of science in university education', *Lancet* 2: 1688.

'Medical aspects of the Russo-Japanese War', *BMJ* 1: 1395–6.

'Metropolitan Hospital Sunday Fund', *Lancet* 2: 1805–6.

'The Mission to Deep Sea Fishermen' (letter with W. H. White, G. K. Hall, J. Langton and T. B. Miller), *The Times* 2 November: 7.

'Speech at Hong Kong', *BMJ* 1: 854.

The Student's Handbook of Surgical Operations, 2nd ed. (with Jonathan Hutchinson, Jr), London: Cassell & Co.; Chicago, IL: W. T. Keener & Co.

'Presidential speech', *Dorset Year Book*, 1904–5, 41–4.

1905

Alcohol: A Poison, London: Church of England Temperance Society.
Alcohol: Its Effects on the Human System from the Medical Point of View, London: Church of England Temperance Society.
'The circumstances and treatment of moveable kidney', *Practitioner* 74: 1–13.
'A conception of disease', *BMJ* 2: 1251–4.
'The home of recovery', *Lancet* 1: 489.
The Other Side of the Lantern: An Account of a Commonplace Tour Round the World, London: Cassell & Co.
'The prospects and vicissitudes of appendicitis after operation', *MCT* 88: 431–55.
'Sir F. Treves on doctors' liberality', *Medical Press* 80: 502.
'Sir F. Treves on the army medical service', *The Times* 28 October: 6.
'Sir F. Treves on the physical effects of alcohol', *The Times* 5 May: 3.
'Union of Medical Societies', *MCT* 88: 88, cxcii–iii.

1906

'Army medical reform' (letter), *The Times* 8 June: 9.
'The effect of the operations of the National Service League upon the national health', *The Times* 31 January: 8.
Highways and Byways in Dorset, London: Macmillan & Co.
'Leys School', *The Times* 9 June: 12.
'National Health Society', *The Times* 22 May: 3.
The Other Side of the Lantern, pop. ed., London: Cassell & Co.
'Physical culture', *The Times* 22 May: 4.
The Physical Effects of Alcohol, London: Richard J. James, Central Temperance Book Room.
'The purity of milk and meat, *The Times* 30 October: 8.
'Sir F. Treves on the bases of success', *The Times* 23 February: 15.
'Sir F. Treves at Islington', *The Times* 18 June: 8.
'Presidential speech', *Dorset Year Book*, 1906–7: 36–7.

1907

'Address to the Royal National Mission to Deep Sea Fishermen', *Toilers of the Deep* 22: 135–6.
'The Army and Navy Male Nurses Cooperation' (letter with H. H. Tooth), *The Times* 21 November: 7.
'Barbados as a winter resort', *The Times* 31 January: 8.
Highways and Byways in Dorset, abridged ed., London: Macmillan & Co.
'Navy and Army Male Nursing Association', *The Times* 4 June: 14.
'The Red Cross Society', *The Times* 2 December: 10.
'The Royal Dental Hospital and School', *The Times* 19 October: 6.
'Sir Frederick Treves and the public', *Medical Press* 83: 694.
'Sir Frederick Treves on the prophylaxis of disease', *Lancet* 1: 1736.

Surgical Applied Anatomy, 5th ed. (with Arthur Keith), London: Cassell & Co.

1908

The Cradle of the Deep: An Account of a Voyage to the West Indies, London: Smith, Elder & Co.
'Evidence of Sir Frederick Treves', Research Defence Society, c.1908.
'To the students of Aberdeen University' (letter), *BMJ* 2: 1586.
'Preventive medicine at Panama', *Proceedings of the Royal Society of Medicine* 1: 303–13.
'The Territorial Army Medical Corps' (letter), *BMJ* 1: 653.

1909

'A lecture on radium in surgery', *BMJ* 1: 317–19.
A Manual of Operative Surgery, 2 vols, 3rd ed. (with Jonathan Hutchinson, Jr), London: Cassell & Co.
'The Red Cross Society', *The Times* 11 August: 7.
'Sir F. Treves and the Red Cross Society', *The Times* 5 June: 7.
'Sir F. Treves on patriotism', *The Times* 15 January: 10.
'Sir F. Treves on the new organization', *The Times* 18 August: 6.
'Are we losing the use of our hands?' *Liverpool Courier* 22 October: 8.
'Sir Thomas Smith, Bart., K.C.V.O., F.R.C.S., Hon. Serjeant-Surgeon to H.M. The King, etc' (obituary), *BMJ* 2: 1104.

1910

'Are we losing the use of our hands?' *Nineteenth Century and After* 67: 461–7.
The Cradle of the Deep, pop. ed., London: Smith, Elder, & Co.
Preface to *Syphilis: Its Diagnosis and Treatment*, F. J. Lambkin, London.
'The prevention of consumption', *The Times* 24 June: 8.
'Puddletown Church' (letter), *The Times* 2 March: 13.
'Sir F. Treves and Red Cross Work', *The Times* 12 July: 16.
'Sir F. Treves and the Red Cross Society', *The Times* 16 April: 13.
Uganda For a Holiday, London: Smith, Elder & Co.
'Voluntary Aid Detachments' (letter), *Lancet* 2: 1516.

1911

Are We Losing the Use of Our Hands?, London: Vineyard Press.
'On hospitals', *The Times* 28 March: 10.
'Red Cross Work', *The Times* 15 July: 5.
'Sir F. Treves on colonial nursing', *The Times* 26 May: 6.
'Speech at the Annual General Meeting of the Research Defence Society', *Lancet* 2: 32.
The Student's Handbook of Surgical Operations, 3rd ed. (with Jonathan Hutchinson, Jr), London: Cassell & Co.
Surgical Applied Anatomy, 6th ed. (with Arthur Keith), London: Cassell & Co.

1912

Alcohol and the Doctors (with T. D. Crothers and A. Lambert), New York: National Temperance Society.
'Antivivisection in Glasgow' (letter), *BMJ* 2: 1578.
'The British Red Cross', *The Times* 10 December: 7.
'British Red Cross and the Balkan Fund' (letter with E. A. Ridsdale), *The Times* 30 October: 7.
The Land That is Desolate: An Account of a Tour in Palestine, London: John Murray.
'Lister', *LHG* 18: 171–2.
The Tale of a Field Hospital, new ed., London: Cassell & Co.
Surgical Applied Anatomy, 6th ed. (with Arthur Keith), Philadelphia, PA: Lea Bros & Co.

1913

The Country of 'The Ring and the Book', London: Cassell & Co.
The Land That is Desolate, pop. ed., London: Smith, Elder, & Co.
'Radium as a curative agent', *The Times* 3 October: 6.
'Sir Jonathan Hutchinson as a teacher', *LHG* 20: 1–2.
'Speech at the opening of the Wellcome Historical Medical Museum', *BMJ* 1: 1380.
Uganda For a Holiday, pop. ed., London: John Murray.

1914

Treves-Keith chirurgische Anatomie, Berlin: Julius Springer Verlag.
'The British Red Cross Society's Hospital at Netley', *The Times* 3 December: 11.
The Country of 'The Ring and the Book', New York: Funk & Wagnalls.
'English-Italian Medical Terms', *BMJ* 1: 1164.
'Hospitals in France', *The Times* 23 December: 10.
'The influence of enforced dogmatism in medicine', *BMJ* 2: 697–701.
The Influence of Enforced Dogmatism in Medicine, Birmingham: Birmingham and Midland Institute.
'Sir Francis Laking, Bart., G.C.V.O., K.C.B.' (obituary), *BMJ* 1: 1217.
'Sir Frederick Treves and the blind', *The Times* 2 April: 11.
'Sir Frederick Treves's offer', *The Times* 1 October: 6.
'Three Dorset doctors', *Dorset Year Book*, 1914–15, 3–9.

1915

'Anti-typhoid inoculation' (letter), *The Times* 26 January: 9.
'Beer with dinner in Red Cross Hospitals', *BMJ* 1: 748.
'The Brassard Bearers', *Times Red Cross Supplement* 21 October: 3.
'£800,000 from "our day"', *The Times* 9 December: 4.
'In sick bay: Boulogne under the Red Cross', *The Times* 25 January: 12.
'Winged pestilence: insects as carriers of disease' (letter), *The Times* 6 July: 6.

'The wounded from the Dardanelles', *The Times* 9 July: 9.

1916

'Disabled fighting men', *The Times* 19 January: 5.
'Hospital work for women doctors', *The Times* 9 June: 5.
'A plea for the wounded', *The Times* 1 February: 9.
Made in the Trenches (with G. Goodchild), London: G. Allen & Unwin.
'The "Star and Garter"' (letter), *The Times* 6 June: 9.

1917

'Gunshot wounds of the abdomen', *BMJ* 1: 377–8.
'Sir Benjamin Franklin, K.C.I.E., etc.' (obituary), *BMJ* 1: 281.
'The "Star and Garter," Richmond: A permanent home for paralyzed and
    disabled sailors and soldiers', *American Journal of the Care of the Crippled* 5:
    146–8.
'Dorset seventy years ago', *Dorset Year Book*, 1917–18, 3–13.

1918

'On writing with the left hand', *BMJ* 1: 16.
Surgical Applied Anatomy, 7th ed. (with Arthur Keith and W. C.
    Mackenzie), London: Cassell & Co.; Philadelphia, PA: Lea Bros & Co.

1919

'Plato on democracy' (letter), *The Times* 30 June: 8.
'A tribute to a great woman', *LHG* 22: 223–5.
'Unaltered Richmond Park', *The Times* 4 April: 9.

1921

The Riviera of the Corniche Road, London: Cassell & Co.
'The "sport" at Monte Carlo', *The Times* 5 April: 11

1922

'Evian: Charms of a Lakeside Town', *The Times* 14 June: 11.
The Lake of Geneva, London: Cassell & Co.

1923

'Cancer and diet' (letter), *The Times* 19 September: 11.
The Elephant Man and Other Reminiscences, London: Cassell & Co.
The Riviera of the Corniche Road, 2nd ed., London: Cassell & Co.

1924

The Student's Handbook of Surgical Operations, 4th ed. (with Jonathan
    Hutchinson, Jr), London: Cassell & Co.

1926

Surgical Applied Anatomy, 8th ed. (rev. C. C. Choyce), London: Cassell &
    Co.

1927

Surgical Applied Anatomy, 8th ed. (rev. C. C. Choyce), Philadelphia, PA: Lea & Febiger.

1928

The Elephant Man and Other Reminiscences, pocket ed., London: Cassell & Co.
The Other Side of the Lantern, pocket ed., London: Cassell & Co.

1929

The Country of 'The Ring and the Book', pocket ed., London: Cassell & Co.

1930

'Richmond Park' (letter) in Sir John Bland-Sutton, *The Story of a Surgeon*, London, 140–1.
The Student's Handbook of Surgical Operations, 5th ed. (rev. C. Wakeley), London: Cassell & Co.

1931

The Student's Handbook of Surgical Operations, 5th ed. (rev. C. Wakeley), New York: Hoeber.

1934

Surgical Applied Anatomy, 9th ed. (rev. C. C. Choyce), London: Cassell & Co.; Philadelphia, PA: Lea & Febiger.

1935

Highways and Byways in Dorset, 2nd ed., London: Macmillan & Co.

1939

The Student's Handbook of Surgical Operations, 6th ed. (rev. C. Wakeley), London: Cassell & Co.; New York: Hoeber.
Surgical Applied Anatomy, 10th ed. (rev. L. Rogers), London: Cassell & Co.; Philadelphia, PA: Lea & Febiger.

1943

The Student's Handbook of Surgical Operations, 7th ed. (rev. C. Wakeley), London: Cassell & Co.

1946

The Student's Handbook of Surgical Operations, 8th ed. (rev. C. Wakeley), London: Cassell & Co.

1947

Surgical Applied Anatomy, 11th ed. (rev. L. Rogers), London: Cassell & Co.; Philadelphia, PA: Lea & Febiger.

1950

The Student's Handbook of Surgical Operations, 9th ed. (rev. Sir C. Wakeley), London: Cassell & Co.

1951

The Student's Handbook of Surgical Operations, 9th ed. (rev. Sir C. Wakeley), New York: Hoeber.

1961

'The Case of Sir John Millais', *Annals of the Royal College of Surgeons* 28: 384–8.
'The Case of Sir Henry Irving', *Annals of the Royal College of Surgeons* 29: 265–8.

1973

'The Case of Sir John Millais', *LHG* 76 (4): 12–15.

1974

'The Case of Sir Henry Irving', *LHG* 77 (2): 11–13.

1980

The Elephant Man and Other Reminiscences, London: Star Books.

1981

Highways and Byways in Dorset, London: Wildwood House.

BIBLIOGRAPHY
OF
WORKS CONSULTED

Abraham, J. Johnston (1958) *Surgeon's Journey*, London: Heinemann.
Altick, Richard (1981) 'Pity the poor monsters', *London Review of Books* 18 December–21 January: 3–5.
Amery, L. S. (gen. ed.) (1900–9) *The Times History of the War in South Africa*, 7 vols, London: Sampson, Low, Marston & Co.
Anon (1891) 'Mr. Frederick Treves, F.R.C.S', *Toilers of the Deep* 6: 224.
—— (1899) 'Mr. Frederick Treves, F.R.C.S. in South Africa', *Toilers of the Deep* 14: 319–21.
—— (1883) Review of Treves's *Surgical Applied Anatomy*, *BMJ* 2: 1076.
—— (1924) 'Sir Frederick Treves: His work for the Mission', *Toilers of the Deep* 39: 14.
Bankoff, George (1947) *The Story of Surgery*, London: Arthur Barker.
Barton, E. A. (1941) *A Doctor Remembers*, London: Seeley, Service & Co.
Battiscombe, Georgina (1969) *Queen Alexandra*, London: Constable.
Best, S. H. (1938) *The Story of the British Red Cross*, London: Cassell & Co.
Bett, W. R. (1953) 'Sir Frederick Treves, Bart.', *Annals of the Royal College of Surgeons* 12: 189–93.
—— (1956) *Sir John Bland-Sutton 1855–1936*, Edinburgh and London: E. & S. Livingstone.
Bishop, W. J. (1960) *The Early History of Surgery*, London: Robert Hale.
—— (1938) 'Sir Frederick Treves and appendicitis', unpub. ts, Wellcome Institute Library London, 5 pp.
Bland-Sutton, John (1930) *The Story of a Surgeon*, London: Methuen.
Bloch, Marc (1973) *The Royal Touch* (tr. J. E. Anderson), London: Routledge & Kegan Paul.
Boase, Frederick (1965) *Modern English Biography*, 3 vols, London: Frank Cass.
Brooks, Stewart M. (1969) *McBurney's Point: Man Against His Appendix*, South Brunswick, NJ and NY: A. S. Barnes & Co.
Brown, G. H. (1955) *Munk's Roll Vol. IV: Lives of the Fellows of the Royal College of Physicians of London 1826–1925*, London: Royal College of Surgeons.

Burdett-Coutts, William (1900) 'Our wars and our wounded', *The Times* 11
April, 27 June, 30 June.
(1900) *The Sick and Wounded in South Africa*, London: Cassell & Co.
Butler, Lewis (1909) *Sir Redvers Buller*, London: Smith, Elder.
Clark-Kennedy, A. E. (1963) *The London: A Study in the Voluntary Hospital
System*, 2 vols, London: Pitman Medical.
(1966) 'The London hospitals and the rise of the university' in F. N. L.
Poynter (ed.) *The Evolution of Medical Education in Britain*, London:
Pitman Medical, 111–20.
Cope, V. Zachary (1950) 'Appendicitis' in Lord Horder (ed.) *The British
Encyclopaedia of Medical Practice*, 2nd ed., London: Butterworth & Co.
(1959) *The History of the Royal College of Surgeons of England*, London:
Anthony Blond.
Crawfurd, Raymond (1911) *The King's Evil*, Oxford: Clarendon Press.
Crocker, H. Radcliffe (1905) *Diseases of the Skin*, 3rd ed. vol. 2, London:
Lewis.
Darbyshire, Taylor (1937) *King George VI: An Intimate and Authentic Life*,
London: Hutchinson.
Delmé-Radcliffe, Francis (1908) *A Lay of the Earl's Chamber: or, the Legend of
the Alderwasley Ram*, Vienna: privately printed.
Delmé-Radcliffe, Frederick Peter (1939) *The Noble Science*, London:
Rudolph Ackerman.
Dugdale, Giles (1953) *William Barnes of Dorset*, London: Cassell & Co.
Esher, Reginald Viscount (1927) *Cloud Capp'd Towers*, London: John
Murray.
(1934) *Journals and Letters of Reginald Viscount Esher*, 2 vols (ed.) Maurice
Brett, London: Ivor Nicholson & Watson.
Faber, Richard (1966) *The Vision and the Need: Late Victorian Imperialist Aims*,
London: Faber.
Farwell, Byron (1977) *The Great Boer War*, London: Allen Lane.
Fitz, Reginald H. (1886) 'Perforating inflammation of the vermiform
appendix', *American Journal of the Medical Sciences* 92: 321–46.
Flower, Sir Newman (1945–6) 'Dorset's greatest surgeon: some memories
of Sir Frederick Treves', *Dorset Year Book*, 5–12.
(1954–5) 'Our first president: some recollections of Sir Frederick
Treves', *Dorset Year Book* 17–21.
(1929) 'Some recollections of Sir Frederick Treves', *Dorset Year Book*,
16–21.
(1939–40) 'Three great sons of Dorset: II. Sir Frederick Treves', *Dorset
Year Book*, 11–14.
(1950) *Just As It Happened*, London: Cassell.
Fussell, Paul (1980) *Abroad: British Literary Travelling Between The Wars*,
Oxford: Oxford University Press.
Gittings, Robert (1980) *The Older Hardy*, Harmondsworth: Penguin.
Graham, Harvey (1956) *Surgeons All*, 2nd ed., London: Rich & Cowan.
Grenfell, Sir Wilfred (1922) *A Labrador Doctor*, pop. ed., London: Hodder
& Stoughton.
(1929) *A Labrador Doctor*, rev. pop. ed., London: Hodder & Stoughton.

(1909) 'Sir Frederick Treves', *Toilers of the Deep* 24: 84–5.

Grosskurth, Phyllis (1980) 'A spectacle of suffering', *Times Literary Supplement* 28 March: 349–59.

Halsted, D. G. (1959) *Doctor in the Nineties*, London: Christopher Johnson.

Hardy, Florence Emily (1962) *The Life of Thomas Hardy, 1840–1928*, London: Macmillan.

Hart, E. P. (ed.) (1936) *Merchant Taylors' School Register, 1561–1934*, vol. 2.

Hibbert, Christopher (1982) *The Court At Windsor: A Domestic History*, Harmondsworth: Penguin.

H. M. R. (1923) 'Sir Frederick Treves' (obituary), *London Hospital Gazette*, 27: 98–100.

Holland, Sydney *see under Knutsford, Viscount*

Holt, Edgar (1958) *The Boer War*, London: Putnam.

Hone, Joseph (1939) *The Life of Henry Tonks*, London: Heinemann.

Howell, Michael and Ford, Peter (1980) *The True History of the Elephant Man*, Harmondsworth: Penguin.

Hutchinson, Herbert (1946) *Jonathan Hutchinson*, London: Heinemann Medical.

J. E. S. (1961) 'Sons of Dorset: Sir Frederick Treves', *Dorset Evening Echo* 15 July.

J. M. (1923) 'Obituary of Sir Frederick Treves', *The Red Cross* 10 (12): 1.

Keith, Sir Arthur (1950) *An Autobiography*, London: Watts & Co.

Kerry, J. Lennox (1959) *Wilfred Grenfell: His Life and Work*, London: Harrap.

Keynes, Sir Geoffrey (1978) *The Life of Sir William Harvey*, Oxford: Clarendon Press.

Knot, Olive (1976) 'The Dorset man who took out a King's appendix', *Dorset Evening Echo* 8 April.

Knutsford, Viscount (Sidney Holland) (1926) *In Black and White*, London: Edward Arnold.

Kuhn, Joy *et al.* (1980) *The Elephant Man: The Book of the Film*, London: Virgin Books.

Lake, Norman C. (1962) 'Treves's Surgical Anatomy', *British Medical Journal* 1: 1813.

Lee, Sir Sidney (1925) *King Edward VII: A Biography*, 2 vols, London: Macmillan.

Le Vay, David (1956) *The Life of Hugh Owen Thomas*, Edinburgh and London: E. & S. Livingstone.

Leyland, John (1888) *Contemporary Medical Men and Their Work*, 2 vols, Leicester: Provincial Medical Journal.

Lloyd, Wyndham E. B. (1968) *A Hundred Years of Medicine*, London: Gerald Duckworth & Co.

Loyd, A. K. (1917) *An Outline of the History of the British Red Cross Society*, London: British Red Cross Society.

McKay, W. J. Stewart (1922) *Lawson Tait: His Life and Work*, London: Baillière, Tindall & Cox.

Magnus, Sir Philip (1977) *King Edward the Seventh*, London: John Murray.

Maurice, Sir John Frederick *et al.* (1906–10) *A History of the War in South Africa*, 4 vols, London: Hurst & Blackett.

Meade, Richard (1968) *An Introduction to the History of General Surgery*, Philadelphia, PA: W. B. Saunders.

Meredith, W. A. (1890) 'An address on the present position of abdominal surgery', *Transactions of the Medical Society of London* 13: 427–8.

Merrington, W. R. (1976) *University College Hospital and Its Medical School: A History*, London: Heinemann.

Millington, Douglas (1979) 'On the road to Mandalay: Travels of Sir Frederick Treves', *Country Life* 14 June: 1938–40.

Moloney, G. E. (1962) 'Operation coronation', *Oxford Medical School Gazette* 14 (3): 141–50.

Montagu, Ashley (1972) *The Elephant Man: A Study in Human Dignity*, London: Alison & Busby.

Monro, Thomas K. (1951) *The Physician as a Man of Letters, Science, and Action*, London: Livingstone.

Montgomery-Smith, E. C. (1961) 'Recollections of an old Londoner', *London Hospital Gazette* 64: 105.

Morris, E. W. (1926) *The London Hospital*, 3rd ed., London: Edward Arnold.

—— (1979) *London Pride: The Story of a Voluntary Hospital*, London: Hutchinson Benham.

Morris, Robert T. (1935) *Fifty Years a Surgeon*, London: Geoffrey Bles.

Morrison, Hyman (1941) 'Reginald Heber Fitz', *Bulletin of the History of Medicine* 10: 250–9.

—— (1946) 'The chapter on appendicitis in a biography of Reginald Heber Fitz', *Bulletin of the History of Medicine* 20: 259–69.

Mulcock, Don (1980) 'Surgeon who saved the king's life', *Western Gazette* 29 August.

Newman, Charles (1957) *The Evolution of Medical Education in the Nineteenth Century*, London: Oxford University Press.

Oliver, Dame Beryl (1966) *The British Red Cross in Action*, London: Faber.

Panton, Sir Philip (1951) *Leaves From a Doctor's Life*, London: William Heinemann.

Peterson, M. Jeanne (1978) *The Medical Profession in Mid-Victorian London*, Berkeley, CA and London: University of California Press.

Plarr, Victor G. (rev. Sir D'Arcy Power *et al.*) (1930). *Plarr's Lives of the Fellows of the Royal College of Surgeons of England*, 2 vols, Bristol: John Wright & Sons.

Ponsonby, Sir Frederick (1951) *Recollections of Three Reigns*, London: Eyre & Spottiswoode.

Power, Sir D'Arcy (1935) 'Treves's first appendix operation', *British Journal of Surgery* 23: 1–3.

Poynter, F. N. L. (ed.) (1966) *The Evolution of Medical Education in Britain*, London: Pitman Medical.

Rivington, Walter (1879) *The Medical Profession*, Dublin: Fanin; rev. and enlarged ed., 1888.

Roberts, Cecil (1932) *Alfred Fripp*, London: Hutchinson & Co.

Samuel, Ralph (1981) 'The elephant man as a fable of class', *New Society*, 19 November: 315–17.

Schofield, A. T. (n.d.) *Behind the Brass Plate*, London: Sampson, Low, Marston & Co.

Selby, John (1969) *The Boer War: A Study in Cowardice and Courage*, London: Arthur Barker.

Shepherd, John A. (1954) 'Acute appendicitis: A historical survey', *Lancet* 2: 299–302.

(1956) 'Lawson Tait and acute appendicitis', *Lancet* 2: 1301–3.

(1965) *Spencer Wells*, Edinburgh and London: E. & S. Livingstone.

Smith, Samuel J. (1932) (letter) *Lancet* 1: 1286.

Thomas, Hugh Owen (1888) *Contributions to Surgery and Medicine, Part VI: The Collegian of 1666 and the Collegians of 1885: or What is Recognized Treatment?*, 2nd ed., London: H. K. Lewis.

Thorwald, Jurgen (1957) *The Century of the Surgeon*, London: Thames & Hudson.

Truax, Rhoda (1947) *Joseph Lister: Father of Modern Surgery*, London: Harrap.

Wangensteen, Owen and Sarah (1978) *The Rise of Surgery*, Minneapolis, MI: University of Minnesota Press.

Watson, Francis (1950) *Dawson of Penn*, London: Chatto & Windus.

Williams, Harley (1949) *The Healing Touch*, London: Jonathan Cape.

INDEX

215